I BELIEVE GOD

ST. PAUL LOOKS BACK
ON HIS LIFE

I BELIEVE GOD

ST. PAUL LOOKS BACK ON HIS LIFE

Noel Davidson

AMBASSADOR

BELFAST, NORTHERN IRELAND
GREENVILLE, USA

I Believe God
© Copyright 2001 Noel Davidson

ISBN 1 84030 111 2

Ambassador Publications
a division of
Ambassador Productions Ltd.
Providence House
Ardenlee Street,
Belfast,
BT6 8QJ
Northern Ireland
www.ambassador-productions.com

Emerald House
427 Wade Hampton Blvd.
Greenville
SC 29609, USA
www.emeraldhouse.com

ACKNOWLEDGEMENTS

The author would like to acknowledge the help and support of the following during the research and writing of this book.

My wife, Liz
Whose patience is endless,
Whose talents are numerous,
And whose constant companionship is priceless.

Professor Dr. Gordon S. Beck,
European Theological Seminary, Birmingham, England.

Dr. Samuel Lowry,
Ambassador Productions, Belfast, Northern Ireland, and Greenville,
South Carolina, USA.

Mr. Norman Mc Call, LL.B.,
Larne, Northern Ireland.

Dr. Nikolas Oikinomou,
Aristotle University of Thessaloniki, Greece.

Professor Alan R. Woodside,
University of Ulster, Jordanstown, Northern Ireland.

CONTENTS

PREFACE

'For I am the least of all the apostles and I am not even fit to be called an apostle, because I persecuted the church of God.'

So said possibly the greatest of all the apostles, who by Divine inspiration wrote almost half of the New Testament! And if he said that of himself, what chance is there for me, in the light of some of his literary masterpieces, to write yet another book about him?

Nevertheless over the years I have been fascinated by this character, the apostle Paul, and have read, talked and even preached, often about him, his conversion, his actions, and his writings. It could be argued that Paul contributed more to the spread of the Gospel, and the establishment of the Christian church on earth, than any other mortal man.

Since I began writing, more than ten years ago, I have endeavoured to write in a style that most people enjoy reading. In fact someone told me recently that I had 'created a reading culture' for they had heard of at least half a dozen people, who had never read a book right through in their lives, but had finished one of mine!

In a combination of those two factors, my life-long interest in the life and times of Paul the apostle, and my desire to write widely readable material, I have attempted in this book to present the life of Paul in a manner, which to my knowledge, has never been done before.

This is Paul's story as I imagine he would have told it himself.

The challenge of this has been to enter the mind of one of the cleverest men who ever graced our planet, and to live with him through a lifetime of experience in the loyal service of his Lord, feeling how he felt, thinking how he thought, and then writing it all down.

What was it like, for example, when after his conversion he went up from Damascus to Jerusalem to see Peter, and Peter, for very understandable reasons, didn't want to see him? Or what did it feel like to be stoned in Lystra, flogged in Philippi, ignored in Athens, despised by the Christians in Corinth, and shipwrecked in the Mediterranean, all in the cause of Christ?

To ensure that this book is, as far as possible, both scripturally and historically accurate, has meant exhaustive study. Many hours reading the Bible, plus books and commentaries by all sorts of authors have gone into it. The travel and research involved have, however, afforded many memorable moments as well. I counted it a thrill, for instance, to stand with my friend Alan Woodside on Mars Hill in Athens, or walk with my wife Liz down the Appian Way, the road along which Paul was escorted into Rome.

Those who are familiar with Bible study type books and commentaries will notice immediately that there are two elements which are common to that sort of work and are absent from this book. These are Scripture references and dates, other than the date which Paul gives himself at the end of his Introduction.

This is deliberate.

I suspected that a multitude of scripture references would jar the flow of the story as Paul tells it, and anyway most of the references I would be using had not been written until he wrote them himself! This book is, however, closely based on the scriptural narrative, and it would be an absorbing exercise for those sufficiently interested, to trace the connections at leisure.

As far as dates are concerned, it is very difficult to be definite in relation to the early Christian church. One of my reference books, 'The Life and Works of St. Paul', by Frederic W. Farrar (1884) includes in the appendix a table showing the chronology of the life of St. Paul as suggested by twenty-six of the established authorities of that time. And not any two of them agree! To make matters worse Farrar himself doesn't agree entirely with any of them, so he makes twenty-seven!

So you can possibly understand why I decided to give dating a miss!

This leads me on to a word for those who are deep theologians and profound Bible students. Should you find in this volume anything which does not fit in with your perception of what actually happened in the life of St. Paul, please don't contact me. Rather I would ask that you forgive me and let us just agree to differ.

In short, and in conclusion, this book is an attempt to make St. Paul both interesting and readable to the vast majority of the people in this world who have never had a Bible commentary in their hands in their lives, and I pray that this may be the outcome of the exercise.

Without further ado then, I will hand you over to 'the apostle and servant of Jesus Christ' himself and let him tell it as it happened. And may I give you a word of advice?

Don't miss his introduction, which follows immediately, for in it he sets the scene for the story.

May you be blessed as you read this book, and may you be able to assert with more assurance, when you are finished, 'I believe God'.

Noel I. Davidson.
September 2001.

INTRODUCTION

It is usually half-dark down here in this prison, and both cold and damp, for most of the time. Very little of the summer sunshine, and even less of the summer heat that Luke tells me they are enjoying in the city these days, ever penetrates.

The Roman authorities have decided to keep me isolated in this holding cell between my trials. I have already been before Nero, and although the jury voted for an adjournment, I feel it is only a matter of time before they trump up some other charge against me and sentence me to death.

Since the great fire in the city nearly two years ago Nero has declared that anyone claiming to be a Christian is committing a crime of disloyalty to the Emperor. He has found some convenient method of blaming the Christian community for the conflagration and is persecuting the believers mercilessly.

As I am considered to be a ringleader of 'this obnoxious sect', as he calls it, I am convinced that he won't rest until he has disposed of me.

My time, I know, is short.

My days, I know, are numbered.

Heaven, I know, is at hand.

So I can't and won't complain.

Even that last trial had its plus points.

Initially, I have to confess, I was rather disappointed that none of the believers in Rome, and there are many of them, either stood up with me, or spoke up for me. On reflection, however, I can understand their position. In the climate that exists here at the present if they had appeared as counsel in my defence, or indeed showed me even the slightest support whatsoever, they could have been the next to face the courts. And the chances are that they could end up, as many of our dear friends have done, as either a flaming torch to light Nero's pleasure gardens, or meat or sport for Nero's lions.

Being compelled to speak in my own defence, then, gave me a wonderful opportunity to state the case for Christ. It was thrilling just to stand there and address the hundreds who had come to witness the trial. The place was packed. These Romans are into the law up to their necks, and nothing gives them more enjoyment, a kind of intellectual entertainment, than to follow the twists and turns of prosecution and defence, in a difficult case.

God told me, right away back at the start, just after I had started out on my career for and with Him, that it was my special job to preach to the Gentiles, and what a chance He gave me to do it that day. It was great.

Nero did his best to appear disinterested, as one would expect from a servant of sin like himself, but there were dozens of others of the common people who were hanging on my every word. It has often been my experience in the past that God uses the truth shared in such circumstances to speak directly to some seemingly insignificant soul.

'My experience in the past', that phrase I have just used, leads me on to explaining the pleasant mental exercise in which I find myself engaged to help pass the long days and the nights which often feel even longer.

Over the past six weeks or so two things have happened which have served to send my mind spinning backwards.

The first of these was that I had a visit from Onesiphorus, a businessman from Ephesus. He had come to the city on a trading trip but took time out to risk his neck to come to see me here. I appreciate this particularly because he could have been arrested for what he did, asking for me all over the city until he was at last directed to this miserable place. It was wonderful to see him, though, and we were able to talk over old times, and he brought me right up to date on what was happening in Ephesus.

And the other thing that sent me into all sorts of reveries was that I have just a few days ago completed and despatched a letter to Timothy. Dear Timothy. How loyal he has been to me since I first came across him as a teenager in Lystra the day they nearly killed me there. I do so much trust that he can get to me again for the winter, that is of course if Nero with his warped mind and mock justice doesn't get to me first.

As I have been sitting and standing by turns here for days, scanning back down the years of my life, I have become increasingly convinced that I should write down some of my own reflections on my many and varied experiences. I know Luke has been working at something like this for years now, for he was always writing away at nights, shut away off alone, no matter where we were, long after everybody had retired for the night. It is my intention, however, to do something different, and that is to record some of my very personal, innermost thoughts. It will be a kind of an autobiography, if you could call it that.

It was a combination of the visit of Onesiphorus, the thought of Timothy, and the present loyal attentions of Luke, my medical consultant, that inspired me to think I should tell this story, with particular reference to some of the tremendous people whom I have met. By that I mean the people who have made a lasting impression, or who have had a powerful influence on me. These impressions and influences range from the grounding I received in the Jewish Scriptures under Gamaliel, to the encouraging words and daring friendship of Barnabas, the hospitality of Lydia and Priscilla and Aquila, and the sterling strength of Silas. That's not to mention the endless discussions with Peter, my on-off-on relationship with Mark, and the times with Titus. There are just so many of them!

I have always loved people, especially the Lord's people.

Since that unforgettable day on the road from Jerusalem to Damascus when I had that illuminated and illuminating encounter with the risen Christ, I have been intensely involved with people, in a variety of ways. Many of these experiences have been pleasant but there have been a few that have proved less so.

There have been only a very few times in my life, like the time in Athens when Timothy and Silas had to go off on urgent business to a couple of the churches in Macedonia, that I have been left on my own, and to be honest I didn't like it. What I would like to do, in this intertwined account of my life and my friends, is tell you about some of the people who have become precious to me, in their own special way. These will be the people God used to help prepare me for His work, to bring and keep me close to Himself, and to comfort me with their companionship in trying times.

The characters who opposed me at every turn, and others who deserted me when I needed them most, I will only mention if I have to in the context of making sense of something else. The God who has been my guard and guide throughout my life knows more about them than I do, so I will leave it to Him to be their ultimate judge.

My mind is absolutely bursting with a multitude of memories of my closest companions, and I want to begin as soon as possible to write them down for anybody who might be interested in reading them in the days to come.

It is important that I start immediately for time is not on my side. There are a couple of very practical factors that could prevent me finishing this absorbing personal project.

The first is that I can only dictate it when I have the services of a scribe, perhaps the overworked but ever willing Luke, or someone else. And the second is that I could be summoned to stand trial in the presence of Nero again, and possibly from there to receive a direct launch into the presence of the Lord whom I love. That will be a glorious release for me if it happens, and the more I think of it the more excited I become. It will be, as I remember telling the friends at Philippi one time in a letter, far better than anything we could dream up or imagine down here. If it happens, however, you will understand that it will bring these fond recollections to an abrupt end. The river of reminiscence will all of a sudden dry up.

You will notice that I have called it, 'I Believe God'. Those words have been a kind of watchword for me in these my later years, since I felt guided to make that affirmation one day in an apparently sinking ship in an apparently endless Mediterranean storm, with everybody panicking around me.

It is to God, and to Him alone I wish to give all the thanks for all that He has done for me and all the glory for all that He has done through me, and my humble prayer from this horrible prison, is that each of you, will either come to know Him if you don't already, or be strengthened in your faith if you do.

I believe God.

Do you?

It is my sincere prayer that God will bless this life story with its underlying theme of meaningful friendship, or as much of it as I manage to complete, to you in the coming days. May you find it as inspirational to read as I have found it challenging to recall and record.

Paul
Rome. June 66.

Chapter One

AT THE FEET OF GAMALIEL

It was marvellous, magnificent, and majestic, all at once.

The golden dome of the Temple gleamed and glistened in the afternoon sun, and having caught my first ever glimpse of the shimmering spectacle, I stood mesmerised.

The journey from Tarsus by sea, and then overland on foot and by shared mule, had been long but I had savoured every second of it. For all along I had been playing mental games with myself, quoting portions from the Sacred Writings in anticipation of that moment, imagining what it would be like.

Nothing, though, could have adequately prepared me for the somehow sanctified splendour of the scene.

There was the road leading down from where we were standing into a valley, then up again through a busy gate into the walls. People of all ages, from Roman soldiers in uniform, to peasant farmers with packs of produce, and parents with their chattering children, streamed steadily from the gate and either strode purposefully or strolled aimlessly along the dusty road. As for the walls, they seemed to stretch on and on forever, with their turrets every so often. And the crowning glory, the dominant feature, the temple, stood in shining state at the throbbing heart of everything, a resplendent reminder of the presence and worship of God in the past, and a refreshing reminder of the purpose of my pilgrimage in the present.

My father, who was normally more impassive than expressive, surprised me by slipping his arm around my shoulder.

"At long last," he said with a soft, satisfied sigh. It sounded to me that he was about to pass on to me all that he had ever owned, or at least see realized all his fondest ambitions for my future. "There it is, Saul, son. Jerusalem. The city of the great King."

Then, almost instinctively, as though the words had triggered something more sublime in his mind, he began to quote a song from the Holy Book.

"Great is the Lord, and greatly to be praised in the city of our God, in the mountain of his holiness," he breathed in hallowed, muted tones.

As he continued speaking, I joined in with him, in even more muted, hallowed tones. I knew the words, too, having learnt them years ago, in The House Of The Book, the synagogue school, back in Tarsus.

" Beautiful for situation, the joy of the whole earth," we continued together, in consecrated chorus, "is mount Zion, on the sides of the north, the city of the great King..."

Then, and as though at the command of some unseen conductor, our voices faded away, into a spellbound, sacred silence.

We stood transfixed together, father and son, savouring the sanctity of our surroundings for many minutes before either of us dared to speak again.

It was father who spoke first, for even if I had wanted to be the one to shatter that silence, I wouldn't have trusted myself to know the right thing to say in the circumstances.

Father did, though.

He had to, for we weren't on a mere sightseeing tour of the Holy City. We were there on business, important business, educational business. And business which father believed would be essential to my life as a Jew, and my future as a Pharisee.

I had been offered a much-coveted place as a pupil of the eminent teacher, Rabban Gamaliel, in the Rabbinical College in the Temple. This College was known and accepted as the finishing school for all fervent Pharisees, so father felt justly proud of me, and was obviously anxious to see me safely into the gentle hands, and under the intense instruction, of the great scholar.

"Come on, Saul, we had better hurry along," he said, suddenly, as though he had just awakened from a distant dream in a pleasant sleep and realized that there was something imminent and important calling out to be done.

With that we set off down the hillside, into the valley, and up the other side. I found myself a few paces behind my father for most of the time.

He was hiking on ahead, looking at nothing, set on catching Gamaliel before he left the Temple, after the hour or prayer.

I was trudging along behind, looking at everything, anxious to meet my new teacher, too, but scared of missing anything on the way!

As we entered in through the gate father slowed down to wait for me. Perhaps he thought I would disappear in the throng of people swarming the narrow streets. It seemed for a few minutes that we were borne along in a tide of bodies, all going in the same direction. And that direction was towards the Temple.

When we passed a tall stone tower, guarded by Roman sentries each with a sword and shield, father informed me, in a hard, matter-of-fact fashion, that it was Antony's Tower where the Roman garrison was housed. Although he was a Roman citizen, and so was I as his son, that seemed to be fine in Tarsus. It was convenient, and respected there. But Roman soldiers standing gazing down into the temple court from the top of that tower seemed to sicken him somewhat.

Antony's tower, though, impressive as it was, soon paled into insignificance when we turned into the vast outer courtyard of the temple. It was a huge place, far bigger than I had ever imagined in my fancies on the journey, and it teemed with people. They were everywhere.

I ended up, walking along, following father, gazing up at the massive marble pillars, whilst trying to avoid becoming too badly bumped about in the process.

Father had already started to climb some steps, with me at his heels, when I saw a stone with some letters carved on it, set into the wall, beside an opening. I was taken aback, initially, to discover that the writing was in Greek, but since I had been brought up in Tarsus conversing in Greek, and my textbook in the House Of The Book had been the Greek version of the Scriptures, I had no trouble reading it.

When I read the message on the stone I stopped in my step, momentarily, for it said,

'LET NO FOREIGNER ENTER WITHIN THE SCREEN AND ENCLOSURE AROUND THE HOLY PLACE. WHOSOEVER IS TAKEN SO DOING WILL HIMSELF BE THE CAUSE THAT DEATH OVERTAKES HIM.'

Surely we were foreigners. Although we were Jews, we had come from a foreign country, we were Roman citizens, and I had been educated in Greek. What a mixture!

When I asked father about it, as he plunged on through the opening without any hesitation whatsoever, he told me that 'The Stone Of Forbidding' as he called it, didn't apply to us, for we were Jews, of the tribe of Benjamin. And in addition to that he was a Pharisee, and we were there so that I, in the best tradition of the family, and following the concentrated course of instruction upon which I was about to embark, should become one.

It all sounded feasible enough, I had to admit, so I followed along faithfully.

The atmosphere had now changed completely.

We had arrived in the Inner Court, a haven for Jews, and Jews alone. There was a more sombre sensation in there.

In what seemed only a matter of minutes, father found the man he was looking for. And when he did I was introduced to the teacher whose wisdom, whose love of the The Law, and whose ability to bring the best out of me, was to be the dominant feature of the next four or five years of my life.

If the Temple, seen from either outside, or inside, the walls of the Holy City, had proved much more magnificent than all my many daydreams had permitted me to visualize, I had made no mistakes in my preconceived perception of my new teacher.

Gamaliel was exactly as I had imagined him, with long flowing robes, a long black beard becoming flecked with grey, and deep set piercing eyes looking both at me and through me, from beneath a scholarly brow.

It was his smile, though, that won me over straightaway.

"So this is Saul," he said, to my father with that broad smile. Then looking across to address me, he went on to make me feel at home, the welcoming smile never leaving his lips.

"And what age are you, Saul?" he enquired, by way of openers.

"Fourteen, almost fifteen," I replied, wondering if that was either too old, or too young, to become a pupil of this learned man.

"Just the ideal age," he went on to encourage me. "I have heard so many good reports of you, I have been waiting to meet you, and have you join us. Your ability to learn the Holy Word in the *mishnah*, the oral repetition, is exceptional apparently. I will show you to your quarters, where you will be staying, and tomorrow you will join the others in my class."

As we walked to my quarters, where I was to live with some other students, most of whom I discovered to be older than myself, my father and my tutor talked incessantly, about points of the Law. I loved the Law just like them, but at that moment I was far too excited to apply my bubbling brain to anything.

That had been a momentous day in my life. And it was only the start of my many momentous days. There were many more to come, even during those student days in the Temple class of Gamaliel.

Next morning I was up early, determined not to miss a minute of life in the Holy City. I wanted to revel in the atmosphere, feel a part of the place, right from hour one of day one.

As I walked along with a few of my fellow-students who had undertaken to escort me to and from The House Of Interpretation, as the temple college was called, I found my attentions divided down the middle as they had been the day before. One eye and one ear seemed to be drawn to the gesticulations and deductions of my guides as they debated some obscure point of the law, while the other eye and ear were busily engaged in trying to catch what my friends didn't seem to be in the slightest concerned at missing. That was the colourful bustle taking place all around them as many of the city's many inhabitants, men and women, Roman soldiers and the Jewish populace, eased themselves into another day.

My initial experience of the rabbinical school, that first morning, I found rather intimidating. For I have to admit that although I had been looking forward to, probably even longing for it, for years, I felt nervous now that my big moment had finally arrived.

When I entered with the others Gamaliel was waiting and welcomed me with the same warmth as he had shown the previous afternoon, and pointed to a vacant place. To say a seat would be overstating it, for my place was a spot on a mat on the floor where I could sit alongside some of the other younger lads. The older students sat around us on a series of short low benches, formed into in a semicircle.

This entire concentration of eager intellectual talent all faced a raised dais on which Gamaliel was soon to assume his position on a chair with long legs which had all the dignity, but none of the elaborate decoration, of a throne.

The instruction that day, and every day as I was to discover, was totally based on the Pentateuch, the Prophecies and the Psalter of the sacred Scriptures. A student read out a passage from a scroll of his own, or our tutor's, choice, and Gamaliel gave his interpretation of it. Then, when he had finished, he invited his students to offer their comments, or perhaps an alternative interpretation of it. The instruction was both intensive and inclusive. Everybody was expected to know the subject in depth, and everybody was expected to participate in the lively exchange of views.

Everyone took part on that, my first day, except one. And I have to confess that I was the sole non-participant.

Rabban Gamaliel had told me that for the first few days I could listen to the discussions and learn the procedures and when I felt comfortable I could contribute.

It was deemed such a privilege to be educated in this company, that within a few weeks I could contain myself no longer and began to air my views, and display my knowledge of and zeal for the Holy Book and the 'traditions of the fathers'.

And before the end of my first full year there I found it complimentary, but also rather curious and occasionally a bit embarrassing, that our revered teacher would consult me for an authoritative statement on some matter, rather than one of the second or third year students. This was perhaps because I loved the scriptures and the ancient writings of our nation, and gave myself whole-heartedly to the study of them. I was the sort of student that if I came upon some difficult problem of interpretation I would wrestle with it all night, to be ready to hold forth on it next day, rather than going to bed!

For the next four years of my life it was my privilege to study under the direction of Gamaliel, and in those years I developed a sincere respect for that kindly teacher. I hadn't been long under his instruction when I learnt of the name by which he was known amongst the other teachers of our nation. Gamaliel was called 'The Beauty of The Law', and I can understand why. He was so gracious and yet so sincere in all his teachings.

In my years in the House of Interpretation I learnt much from him. I learnt how to reason out the sense and proper application of a passage, and I was encouraged to cultivate at least a passing acquaintance with the work of some Greek scholars, although I was later to learn that this perceived 'liberalism' was frowned upon by some of the more fundamental Rabbis in the temple.

Gamaliel's chief contribution, though, to my becoming a fervent Pharisee was his unquestionable love and zeal for 'the oracles of God'. This fervour was infectious, and I became smitten with it, to what many would describe as a fanatical extent.

It came to the point, indeed, that some who knew me thought that I was not behaving as a student of the gentle Gamaliel but as someone who had studied under one of the more hard-line exponents of the law! I had outstripped my tutor in ardent zeal!

During those formative years in Jerusalem this evolving enthusiasm for Jewish law, Jewish traditions and my Jewish identity caused me to project my mind forward to the future prospect for all things Jewish. And this in turn did two things for me as a young man resident in the glorious capital of our God-chosen nation.

It caused me to harbour a bitter resentment of the Roman soldiers, those servants of a vast and oppressive alien empire, who were encamped in, marching all over, and attempting to impose their heathen laws and customs upon, this holy land.

This, too, in its turn, compelled me to anticipate the advent of the promised Messiah, the Prince Leader who would come from God to free his people from all repression and injustice.

When discussing the work of the prophet and poet, Isaiah, I used to love to turn my attention, and everybody else's too, when given the chance, to some of the proclamations in relation to our coming King.

With what pride I would proclaim, 'Behold my servant, whom I uphold; mine elect, in whom my soul delighteth; I have put my spirit upon him...'

And with what power I would punch out, 'he shall bring forth judgment to the nations.'

Or one of my favourite passages, which was often read to us by Gamaliel himself, in tones laden with passionate longing, was, 'The Spirit of the Lord God is upon me; because the Lord hath anointed me to preach good tidings unto the meek...To proclaim the acceptable year of the Lord, and the day of vengeance of our God; to comfort all that mourn; To appoint unto them that mourn in Zion, to give unto them beauty for ashes, the oil of joy for mourning, and the garment of praise for the spirit of heaviness...'

What a wonderful day of release, of triumph, and of justice that would be, when our mighty Messiah would crush all his enemies below His feet! In that day we would recover our freedom, our country, our national identity, and our God-given way of worship.

When I finished my studies at The House Of Interpretation and became recognized as a teacher of the law, and a fully-fledged Pharisee, I made the journey back, with the blessing of Gamaliel, to my home city of Tarsus.

It had always been my intention to return to my roots.

I wanted to become an exponent of the oracles of God back in the synagogue where I had received my early grounding in the Holy Scriptures. And I had another fervent aim, also.

The Rabbis taught that if but one person could keep the whole law, without offending in any one point, for just one day, then the troubles of Israel would be ended, and the Messiah at last would come.

Wouldn't it be marvellous if I could be so diligent in my observance of the Law that I could be that man?

And I might even be accorded a position of power in the all-conquering kingdom of the all-conquering King!

Chapter Two

THE FACE OF AN ANGEL

The desire to achieve perfection in my pursuit of righteousness as a diligent Pharisee had by then become the overriding passion of my life. And a growing awareness of what some saw as my ability to interpret the law, and my unquestioned zeal in its observance to the letter, resulted in my recognition as a rabbi in the synagogue in Tarsus.

This position led to a redoubling of my zeal in the study and interpretation of the law and the prophets. I spent days, from morning to night in the synagogue, discussing and disputing the sacred scriptures, and the hundreds of different interpretations and impositions of the law, and the many Messianic prophecies with other Pharisees.

This obsession with the holy law and its ceremonial observances seemed to create more problems for me that it solved, however. For it seemed that the more I learnt of the demands of the law the more difficulty I experienced in the keeping of them.

During those Tarsus years I paid many visits to the weaver's shop where I had learnt the trade of tent making, as a boy. On a number of occasions I did some work to help out, and although the weaving of the black strongly-scented goat's hair into cloth for tents was not rewarding work, it afforded me the opportunity to contact others in an informal setting, talk about the law, and seek vainly to adhere to its every requirement.

The highlights of those years, though, did not occur in Tarsus at all, but in Jerusalem. I made it my practice to return to the holy city, the sacred capital of my religion, as often as I could, and especially at Passover times, if I could arrange it that way. This allowed me to soak up the atmosphere that had been so much a part of my early education, when at Passover the streets just teemed with pilgrims from all corners of the Roman Empire, all anxious to celebrate the feast.

It was during one such visit to the city that I heard some strange and startling news. A carpenter from Nazareth was on a walking tour of the country, performing miracles, talking in parables, and claiming to be the Son of God. The alarming thing about it was that hundreds of the common people were flocking after him, day and daily. Apparently, too, some of the Pharisees whom I knew to be quite well versed in the ancient writings, had tried to challenge him on points of the law, and had ended up rather chastened.

That was only the start of it.

A couple of years later, this Jesus the Nazarene was crucified by the Romans, at the demand of our leaders who were anxious to rid the country of an upstart making such preposterous claims. If that had been the end of him and his teachings, it would have been good, but it wasn't.

His followers caused a sensation in the city when they claimed that he had risen from the dead and that they had seen him. This caused a wave of fanaticism to sweep through the streets.

All the Jewish travellers visiting our synagogue in Tarsus seemed to be able to talk of nothing else. I tried to belittle such gossip but all those who had been in Jerusalem seemed convinced that some sort of a religous upheaval had taken place.

Seemingly one of the followers of the Nazarene, not a Pharisee, or a rabbi, but a fisherman if you please, had stood up boldly one day and publicly proclaimed that this Jesus was the Promised One, The Anointed of God. He even went so far as to accuse the leaders of our nation of rejecting the Messiah, and condemning him to death.

The news, also, that thousands of people, mostly the unlearned, but surprisingly, some of our priests as well, were blindly embracing this heresy, was worrying.

It was crazy, crazy stuff.

For the next year and more the news trickling back to Tarsus became more perturbing to the extent of becoming almost alarming.

These people were organizing themselves into groups for worship and were sharing what they called 'love feasts' together. The more subtle and sinister aspect about this spurious sect, however, was that they had, whilst posing as orthodox Jews, begun to infiltrate the synagogues of the city, promoting their heretical teaching.

And many of the people were believing it!

How could they? How dare they?!

Who could ever accept that a crucified carpenter could be the coming Messiah?

Our law taught, 'Cursed is every one that hangs on a tree'. Jesus the Nazarene had been hung on a tree between two criminals. Was he not cursed then?

A Messiah foretold by our prophets, and cursed by our law!

It was outrageous, ridiculous nonsense.

What a pity that those poor deluded common people hadn't immersed themselves in the law and the prophets to the extent that I had done! If they had, they most certainly would not have imbibed the doctrine of an obscure itinerant conjuror for a few kicks and a share of some bread and wine.

I determined that when Passover next came around I would travel to Jerusalem well before the feast and find out what was happening. If it meant staying in the city for a year or two I would do so. It would be worth it if I could help counter this apostasy and if need be even instigate some sort of a movement to purge our holy places of this potential plague.

When I had the opportunity to put my plan into action, I travelled to Jerusalem, and was shocked to discover that the situation was every bit as bad as I had been led to believe, perhaps even worse.

This new cult was spreading quickly and quietly throughout the city, like some virulent disease.

Another disturbing aspect of it, and one which I had never anticipated, was the increasing number of teachers who were promoting the New Way, as some had dubbed it. They seemed to be appearing from nowhere, on a daily basis. Unlearned and ignorant men were preaching this bogus religion with absolute conviction and a strange, unnatural eloquence.

I decided to begin my campaign to have this heresy eradicated, in the place where it could do most damage if it gained a firm foothold, and that was in the synagogues.

There were many synagogues in Jerusalem, but since some of my fellow-countrymen attended the Synagogue of the Cicilians, I began making it my practice to go there regularly also. And it was there that I started to teach and promote the truth of the still-awaited Messiah with increased fervour, in an attempt to counter the ridiculous claims of the Nazarene.

It was in that synagogue, too, that I first encountered one of the most able, and most ardent, exponents of this rampant religion, a man called Stephen.

Stephen was a Greek-speaking Jew, a Hellenist, but it was not long before the resident rabbis in the Cicilian synagogue realized that he was extremely well read in all the Holy Scriptures. As he stood up to teach, many of us actively opposed his arguments, but we found him to be an accomplished orator. It was peculiar, but there were times when we thought that he was speaking as though directed by a mystical, supernatural power. This merely served to make the situation all the more sinister.

Something would have to be done, and soon.

Every time Stephen chose to speak in the synagogue, others were embracing this phoney faith. There was something about the man, or his message, or both, that was appealing to normally loyal members of the our own God-given religion.

After much murmuring and muttering we devised a plan.

Some of the matters which this Stephen had taught could be construed as blasphemous, and contrary to the Law of Moses. Indeed somebody reported that somebody had said that Stephen had said that Jesus the Nazarene had said that he could destroy our magnificent temple and build it again in three days.

What utter rubbish! What blasphemy!

Within days we had lit fires of dissent about this man Stephen and his teachings in our synagogue, by secretly persuading men to report to the elders of our nation and the members of the Sanhedrin, our concerns about what was going on amongst us. It was our aim that accompanied by a steady breeze of bitterness, this smouldering fire would soon be fanned into all-consuming flames of fury.

We pressed for a full meeting of the ruling body of our religion, the Sanhedrin, to give a decision on the matter urgently, before any more damage was done, and dozens more had rejected the Faith of the Fathers.

It worked.

A meeting of the Sanhedrin was organized and Stephen was summoned to attend. A number of us, who had been so unhappy with his teaching, and so unable to negate his arguments, were quite happy to escort him, calling out as we went, through the Temple Courts to The Hall of Hewn Stone, where the Council of Seventy, The Sanhedrin, had gathered.

The manner in which this ultimate court of appeal in all matters pertaining to our religion, had seated themselves, reminded me, somehow, of my early days at the feet of Gamaliel.

The High Priest, who was The President of the Council of Seventy, occupied a central position, and radiating out into a semicircle on either side of him in descending order of seniority sat the remainder of the seventy. The older members in their brightly coloured robes sat nearest the President, with the younger Scribes at the outer edge on either side.

This august council had assembled in solemn and formal state to try the blasphemer.

Those who had brought Stephen to trial stood around the walls to witness proceedings.

An air of hushed expectancy hung over the place.

At a word from the President the accusers stepped forward, one by one.

And one by one, with stern and serious faces, they poured out a torrent of allegation against the man arraigned before them.

He had been misrepresenting the Law of Moses, they said.

He had been downgrading the Temple, they said.

And worst of all, he had been fostering faith in a crucified Messiah in direct contravention of the most divine hopes of Israel, they said.

I have to confess, however, that I heard little of what they said, for at one stage I had glanced across to see how the defendant was responding to such a catalogue of condemnation. And from that moment I found myself unable to tear my eyes off the man standing submissively in the centre of the semicircle.

It was the glow on his face, which held me transfixed. His countenance was incandescent. His face shone like the face of an angel.

As the hired-out prosecutors rambled on and on, the silent Stephen's face had begun to shine with a strange suffused splendour, and the longer I gazed the more mesmerized I became.

My mind flashed back to the sacred scriptures, and to the story of Moses. When he came down from the mount of God, he had to cover his face with a veil, because of the shine on his skin.

Could this be a sign from God?

No! Perish the thought!

The man before us that day was a false teacher, a heretic, and an apostate.

My attention was diverted away from the captive's radiant face, and my preoccupation with Moses and the Mount brought to an abrupt end, by the voice of the High Priest, addressing the accused, and inviting him to speak forth in his own defence.

"Are there things so?" he enquired.

Obviously pleased to be given the chance to answer the charges which had been brought against him, Stephen began, with great courtesy, addressing the leaders as 'Men, brethren and fathers', in the accepted custom.

There then followed a period when our prisoner took us through an accurate, and comprehensive history of our nation. During this address I found it difficult to decide whether to focus on the fluent speaker, with his hand outstretched and his face still aglow, or to allow my eye to scan around the semicircle, which represented the complete embodiment of Jewish learning and tradition.

It was fascinating to watch the fathers, as they nodded assent at some points, and puckered their brows at others, wondering what was coming next.

But it was even more fascinating to watch the speaker, to contemplate the fervour with which he spoke, and to try to trace the line of his argument.

It was a masterly address, I had to admit.

I felt myself becoming rather uncomfortable, however, when I finally thought I saw what this calmly confident orator was trying to prove. He had, in effect, proved to us that for nearly one thousand years Israel had been God's people, but in all that time they did not have, nor did they appear to need, a permanent temple. Then he went on to point out from the writings of the prophet Isaiah that when at length a temple was built, God had proclaimed its inadequacy by announcing that heaven was His throne, and the earth His footstool. How could mortal man build an appropriate dwelling for an Almighty God?

Some of the senior members of the Sanhedrin, I could see, shared my concern. The speaker was no longer commanding their undivided attention. They had begun to whisper to one another.

This restlessness in his audience seemed to catapult the accused into a complete about turn. For in an instant everything changed.

Suddenly the defendant turned prosecutor.

The man who had been busy outlining the case in his own defence suddenly turned upon the seventy elders who were to act as judge and jury in the case, accusing them of intransigence, unfaithfulness, and ultimately murder.

They had, he asserted with firm conviction, betrayed and murdered the Just One, The Promised One, The Messiah!

This was too much to take, without reply.

Many jeered and sneered, many shouted angry retorts, and many growled their fierce disapproval.

The atmosphere had turned decidedly ugly.

The only person who had retained his composure was the prisoner.

When I looked across at him he was standing, gazing intently upwards, his face resplendent with supernatural light. All of a sudden his strong voice was heard above all the hubbub around him.

"Behold, I see the heavens opened, and the Son of man standing on the right hand of God!" he exclaimed.

That was totally unacceptable to the Sanhedrin. What further utter blasphemy!

Mayhem ensued.

All at once, and as though someone had shouted a command, the seventy men who had been seated, sprang up from their places with their hands over their ears in case they should hear any more heretical nonsense, and rushed towards Stephen. They all seemed to arrive with him at once and they clamoured to grab hold of him to propel him out of the temple, and out of the city.

The Law had decreed that any Israelite who was found guilty of blasphemy should be stoned, so stoned this heretic would have to be.

Such a sentence could not be carried out within the confines of the Temple or the city, though, lest such holy places should be profaned. It must be enacted outside the city walls.

When the crowd of infuriated elders had reached what they considered to be a suitable spot of execution they discarded their colourful robes, anxious to avoid contamination by the blood of such a rebel, and piled them up at my feet, with the growled instruction, "Look after those until we are finished!"

They then proceeded to arm themselves with the jagged rocks that abounded in the rough scrub by the roadside. And in a frenzy they converged upon Stephen for a second time, hurling their rocks at his head.

The glow on the apostate teacher's face was soon dulled by his own blood as it at first trickled slowly, then flowed freely, from a succession of gaping scalp wounds.

It was hard for me to see what happened next from where I was standing at the edge of the crowd, for when he had called out, "Lord Jesus, receive my spirit," Stephen slumped to his knees.

When his self-appointed executioners closed in to finish him off, their flailing bodies blocked him completely from my view.

The last thing I heard was that same strong voice, nothing abated from the Hall of Hewn Stone, crying out for mercy. What surprised me somewhat, though, was that he wasn't craving mercy for himself, but for his killers.

'Lord, do not hold this sin against them!" were his last words.

In a few minutes the crowd around the victim began to thin out backwards idly dropping stones, which were by then surplus to requirements.

I was one of the last to leave the scene that day for I had to wait until the party of executioners had wiped the blood and sweat from themselves as best they could before coming to me to retrieve their cloaks.

Just before I turned to retrace my steps back into the city, I took one last look at the body of Stephen.

It was barely recognizable as that of a human being, having been pounded almost to pulp under the barrage of stones.

'Good job, well done,' I thought.

'One down, and dozens more to go.

Just let me at the rest of them.'

Chapter Three

I AM JESUS

My burning passion to stamp out this heresy, to allow no remaining trace of it to pollute our holy land, and to allow no possible contemplation of it to corrupt the minds of God's holy people, soon led to my promotion.

The religious leaders of our nation, obviously appreciating my obsession with wiping out the followers of 'The Way', as they had the audacity to call it, appointed me to the Sanhedrin.

This was great, for it gave me official approval for my intensifying policy of harassment and oppression. God, I was sure, would be as pleased with me as the High Priest seemed to be. Soon the sect would be no more and we in the Temple and the synagogues could return to our comfortable lifestyles, our endless discussions about the law, and our patient wait for the true, the real, Messiah.

Days rolled into nights, and weeks rolled into months in a blur of frantic activity.

Accompanied by a band of ruthless temple guards, and armed with my authorisation from the Sanhedrin, I raided houses all over the city. If I heard of this detestable sect of the Nazarenes holding one of their meetings anywhere, I burst in on it. And when I did, I had the temple guards, who were not renowned for their delicate handling of detractors from the truth, drag the lot of them before the Council Of Seventy.

In my newly appointed position as a member of that Supreme Court I could not only bring the offenders to trial, but also record my vote against them when it came to reaching a verdict.

Gradually, I thought we were winning.

After a number of these people, both men and women had been publicly scourged and then clapped into prison with some of the more influential, and more eloquent, and therefore potentially more dangerous of them, stoned to death outside the walls, it began to look as though we would soon be rid of them.

I was glad of that, for a host of reasons.

There were now no more preachings and so-called miracles in Solomon's Porch.

There were now no more heresies being publicly propagated in our synagogues.

There were now no more open to all, jam-packed gatherings crammed into stuffy upper rooms.

If there were any of these deluded 'disciples' left, and I could have no doubt but that a few had so far escaped my purge, they had at least been forced to practice their profanity behind closed doors.

All that blasphemy had been abolished from all the public places in our holy city, the earthly site of the Temple of God. And starved of popular support, the obnoxious sect would probably soon peter out, as so many futile rebellions had done before.

Another reason why I would be happy to see the end of this ridiculous faction was that I would be glad to be finished confronting these stubborn people. All of them, and in this respect some of the women were even more difficult to deal with than the men, demonstrated a loyal and unshakeable devotion to the crucified Nazarene. This galling but genuine fidelity seemed to disregard the prophecies of the ancient scriptures in relation to the coming, all-conquering Messiah, and be based solely on a profound but totally inexplicable union of love.

It was virtually impossible to persuade them to renounce this crazy faith.

Just when we thought we had begun to eradicate the plague from our sacred city of Jerusalem, we heard some sickening news.

The followers of the Nazarene had begun to pop up all over the place!

Travellers coming into the capital were reporting that they were beginning to promote their despicable doctrine in synagogues all over the country, and indeed farther afield amongst Jewish settlements across the Roman Empire.

It was desperately irritating.

As I came to contemplate the spread of the sect it made me think of a game that I used to play, years before, with some other boys in the thronged bazaars and markets of Tarsus, my home city. At the close of the day, when the noisy traders were all packing up to head off home we sometimes scouted around spotting, and then stamping on, all the overripe, and discarded fruit, which lay in idle, insect-ridden confusion on the ground.

What I soon discovered was that the harder I stamped on an orange, the flatter it became, and the farther it spread! The squashing process, as well as spreading the orange, left its seeds exposed, to be picked up by the ravening birds that fed when we were in bed. They would then drop them somewhere else, ready to ripen and grow again, miles from Tarsus market.

It really distressed me when I heard about what was happening in Damascus.

Apparently a small, but active and therefore growing, cell of these non-conformists, had begun to surface in the several synagogues there. The Syrian capital had become a hornet's nest of this hateful delusion. If this sect was to be effectively exterminated, it seemed that we were going to have to hunt them down more widely, and more mercilessly.

Within days of hearing this news I had requested an audience with the High Priest. Since the Sanhedrin claimed religious jurisdiction over all Jews, everywhere, I had no trouble persuading him to furnish me with letters of authority to set up a court in a synagogue somewhere in Damascus to accost the dissidents, and then march them in chains back to Jerusalem to be scourged, or stoned, as sentenced.

All that remained for me to do then was select a small band of the most cruelly competent temple guards to accompany me, to help with the return route march of the captured rebels, and a couple of muleteers to carry our tents for the night stopovers, and in two days we set off.

The journey would take between six and eight days, depending on how hard we pushed ourselves. And I was determined to push myself, and my travelling companions, very hard.

The sooner we arrived in Damascus, the sooner we could get to work to round up the religious renegades infesting that city.

The hours spent pressing northward would give me time to decide upon an effective strategy for capturing and convicting the most heretics in the shortest possible time.

As the hot days passed, each one as dry and dusty as the one before it had been, I became beset by occasional doubts. Since I could not converse, in any meaningful manner, with my attendants, my eternally active mind was forced into constant reflection.

I tried to keep all the little jabs of conscience from needling me.

I tried to prevent all the little flashes of memory from nettling me.

But it was difficult.

When we were passing the Sea of Galilee, I found myself drawn, despite my best efforts to prevent myself being drawn, into contemplating the Nazarene. It was around that lake that the carpenter from Nazareth had done a lot of his teaching to fishermen and crowds of the common people, apparently.

And then that carpenter, who claimed to have been the Messiah, had been crucified. Many of his followers, whom I had dragged unceremoniously before the Sanhedrin, had quoted the writings of the prophet Isaiah in defence of his Messianic claim. These bold men, whom I had discovered, to my chagrin, would rather die than lie, had on more than one occasion cited fearlessly, in the presence of my learned colleagues, the words...

'He is despised and rejected of men; a man of sorrows and acquainted with grief: and we hid as it were our faces from him; he is despised, and we esteemed him not. Surely he hath borne our griefs and carried our sorrows: yet we did esteem him stricken, smitten of God and afflicted. But he was wounded for our transgressions, he was bruised for our iniquities: the chastisement of our peace was upon him; and with his stripes we are healed. All we like sheep have gone astray; we have turned every one to his own way; and the Lord hath laid on him the iniquity of us all. He was oppressed and he was afflicted yet he opened not his mouth: ...'

I knew the passage well. I had learnt it as a seven year old in the House of the Book in Tarsus, and discussed it as a seventeen year old in the House of Interpretation in Jerusalem. It had never made much sense to me in the context of a triumphant mighty Messiah, though.

But was it beginning to make sense now?

No. Of course not! It must mean something else. How dare I even allow myself to entertain such a thought?!

There was one night, too, when I couldn't get Gamaliel, my mentor, out of my mind. About a year, before, and just before I came up to Jerusalem to try to help dispense with the followers of the Nazarene, he had given his respected counsel to the Sanhedrin on the subject of the sect, and had, or so it was generally reported, advised the Council to leave them alone! If they were impostors they would perish, he had reasoned, but if they proved genuine then it would be a serious thing to have been seen to fight against God.

When I heard of it then, and thought of it afterwards, I was both surprised and disappointed at this wait-and-see advice from my former tutor. Surely a man like Gamaliel, who had spent his life steeped in the sacred scriptures, ought to have known better!

Or could he have been right after all?

Was I, heading for Damascus, full of holy fury, actually fighting against God?

No! I was nothing of the sort. I was actually fighting *for* God!

On the other hand, those men and women who had submitted to cruel torture without complaint, and had firmly and flatly refused to renounce their faith, hadn't struck me as people who were fighting against God, either.

Then there was Stephen, too.

In moments of quiet reflection, which I refused to afford myself often, but which had been forced upon me on that long, and mentally lonely journey, I thought of him.

"I see the heavens opened," he had said.

"I see the Son of man," he had said.

"Lord, forgive them for this," he had said.

What blasphemy!

Or... was it?

And the sight of that bludgeoned body, bathed in its own blood, still haunted me.

It was all so confusing. So convicting.

It was, however, also, all so stupid of me to permit myself to think such thoughts.

I was a Pharisee, and a member of the Sanhedrin, en route to Damascus to purge the synagogues of a creeping, choking heresy. And my only escape from distracting contemplation was to press on more fiercely in my fervent pursuit.

When we first caught sight of Damascus, early in the morning of what was to be the final day of our journey, I allowed the party to stop for a few moments for a drink from our water bottles, and to survey the scene before us. After all the arid, barren land through which we had passed, it was wonderful to see the white roofs of the buildings already shimmering in the sun. Many beautiful trees, the dark green leaves of which would soon, we hoped, provide us with welcome avenues of shade, surrounded the city nestling below in the verdant valley.

We stopped for a few minutes, but only a few minutes, and then we were on our way again.

Travellers would normally plan to rest, as the hottest part of the day approached, but since we were so close to our destination I decided to press on, despite the mumblings and murmurings of the muleteers. They could rest in the shade when they reached the city, I told them. And every hour, maybe every minute, was precious to me.

If we pressed on I could establish myself in a synagogue and possibly even apprehend a few apostates before nightfall!

As we approached the city I thought of its long history, and its place in our ancient writings. Eliezer, our father Abraham's steward, had come from here. Naaman had wanted to wash in either the Abana or the Pharphar, the rivers we had seen, glinting in the sun, from the ridge above, to cleanse him from his leprosy. And now I was about to write another chapter in the history of the place. I was going to cleanse *it* from something, too…

Then, suddenly, unexpectedly, and absolutely phenomenally, everything changed!

I had always thought that there was nothing that could outshine a Syrian sun at noon, but I was wrong. In that moment it seemed as though the whole atmosphere had caught fire and we were enveloped in white sheets of dazzling splendour.

All of us, my whole party, were involuntarily flung to earth, totally prostrated, by some unseen, powerful, supernatural force.

As I lay there, flattened, all thought of the others who had been travelling with me, immediately vanished from my thoughts. It was as though they had ceased to exist.

I had become acutely aware that I was not alone, in a completely different sense. There was a person whom I had never met before, and a presence, the like of which I had never felt before, near me, and enclosing me.

Then I heard a powerful, but wonderfully placid, voice, call my name in Hebrew. It was the voice of supreme authority, the voice of someone in confident control of the situation.

"Saul, Saul, why are you persecuting me?" it asked.

I lifted my head to try and discover who or what this was. Could I be hearing things? Was I losing my reason?

As I peered into the blinding blaze of brilliance before me I soon discovered that this was no figment of my imagination. I was not mad. Or hallucinating. There *was* a person there! It was a man, resplendent in a heavenly glory.

Stunned, and afraid that this personage was possibly one of the hated heretics whom I had been hunting, but had not yet apprehended, my instinctive reaction was to breathe out in astonished awe, "Who are you, Lord?"

"I am Jesus of Nazareth," the voice continued, gently persuasive.

"It is me whom you are persecuting. It is hard for you to kick against the goads."

The Nazarene! The despised Nazarene!

Jesus of Nazareth, the one whose name I had derided, whose claims I had dismissed, and whose disciples I had detested, was standing, alive, framed in fantastic effulgence, before me!

Suddenly my whole body began to tremble uncontrollably.

The confusion, which had begun to plague my mind, gave way, in that instant, to complete consternation. I had been making one awful, terrible mistake. During those moments of realization, those shocking moments of divine revelation, I was convulsed with fear and anguish.

Then, slowly, as though soothed by some unseen but tender hand, my body ceased from its involuntary shuddering, and an indescribable calm enveloped my mind.

I just went on lying there, motionless, breathless, submissive.

It was strange.

I felt all of a sudden so settled.

All the antagonism and all the animosity, all the hatred and all the hostility, all the rebellion and all the resentment, had vanished, disappeared, like early morning mist before a rising, strengthening sun.

"Lord, what do you want me to do?" I enquired, meekly, scarcely able to manage much more than a whisper.

My new Master responded immediately. He wasted no time in outlining His initial overall blueprint for my life. The one who had proved so diligent in the persecution of His doctrine, was the one whom He had chosen to be every bit as diligent in its proclamation.

"I have a detailed plan for your life," He told me. "You will bear My Name far across the known world to the Gentile nations. But get up now and move on into Damascus. You will be given further directions from there. Arise now, and go!"

Then, almost as suddenly as He had appeared, Jesus of Nazareth, the new Lord of my life, whom I had seen so clearly, disappeared into the glowing atmosphere and choking heat of noonday, and I was left to carry out His instructions.

As I struggled to my feet I became aware of two things. The first concerned my own condition, the second that of my companions, who had begun to crowd around me.

My difficulty was, however, that although I could hear them, I couldn't see them!

I had become possessed with a hitherto unknown serenity of soul, but the light, which had illuminated my soul, had blinded my eyes!

I had been thrown to the ground a bitter man.

I had lain on the ground a broken man.

And now I had risen from the ground, a blind man!

As I heard my retinue discuss the incident which had just occurred, I realized that they hadn't seen what I had seen, or heard what I had heard. They spoke of hearing strange voices, which they couldn't understand, and seeing bright lights, which they couldn't explain. They were, as I had been initially, trying to convince themselves that they hadn't imagined it all!

When I began to stumble forward sightlessly I felt one of the bewildered temple guards grab me by the hand. "It's not far to the city now, master," he said softy. "We will guide you there."

And so it was that I entered the historic city of Damascus, not as someone seeking to injure the followers of The Way, but as someone who had just joined them! Not as a rebellious despiser of Jesus of Nazareth, but as his most recent disciple.

As my guides led me slowly along the wide stone pavement of Straight Street, trying to save me from bumping into everything from merchants' camels to traders' stalls, I could sense the busy buzz of the place, but could see none of it.

I felt so humbled, and yet so happy.

When we came to the house of a man called Judas, where I had arranged to stay, I was glad to grope my way into a back room away from all the bustle. Many people wanted to talk to me, but I didn't want to talk to them, at least for a while.

I could hear the babble of voices in the outer room towards the street, discussing all sorts of propositions in excited tones. Words like 'thunder', 'lightning', 'uncanny', 'hallucination', and 'weird' seemed to be cropping up time and time again.

It required little effort for me to blot them out of my mind, however.

I was the only one who *knew* what had happened.

And I, though, now at peace with myself and strangely close to God, had problems of my own.

How, for instance, could I inform the rabbis in the local synagogues of my complete about face?

There was something even more difficult than that, too.

How could I contact the people whom I had come to capture, and convince them that I was totally changed and wanted to join them?!

And who was going to tell me what I should do next?

What could a blind man, with no real friends, in a foreign city, do for God, or anybody else, anyway?

Chapter Four

BROTHER SAUL

For days I felt strange.

My heart had been overtaken by a peace and satisfaction the like of which I had never before experienced.

But my mind was in a whirl.

Ever since that moment when Jesus revealed Himself to me in the splendour of light on the road outside the city, addressing me, his most outwardly active enemy, with such forgiving grace and such challenging frankness, I had been struggling to come to terms with my present position. My old life, my old person, had been torn up by the very roots, and been replaced, I felt by a totally different me. I was striving to understand this new identity, this new person, this Saul of Tarsus the second.

My first, but by no means, my prime concern, was physical.

I was blind. Would I ever be able to see again? Or was this a judgement of God upon me for my sin of rebellion?

There were even deeper considerations, which soon overshadowed my concerns about my physical condition, however. For although God had shut out from me the everyday happenings of the world around, by striking me blind, He had, in that same instant, opened the inner eyes of my understanding to truths which I had never appreciated before. There I was, someone who had prided himself in his knowledge of the law, finding myself back at square one, a student again. Not this time at the feet of Gamaliel, but at the feet of Christ.

It proved to be a steep, and sharp, learning curve. For everything I had learnt and come to passionately believe, for the previous thirty or so years, since boyhood, I had to accept as having been basically in error. And what I had equally opposed as being nonsense, heresy and blasphemy, I had come, in one split second of glorious revelation, to accept as being the truth of God!

What would Gamaliel think of me, I often wondered in those days? For I had, as a result of one confrontation with Christ, renounced all his teachings on the coming Messiah, and accepted the claims, first preached by a few Galilean fishermen who had never been to a rabbinical school in their lives, that the despised Nazarene was indeed the Promised One of God?

And the High priest, what would he say when he heard about my dramatic somersault in belief? It struck me once that the letters, which I still had somewhere, bearing his signature, were now, in fact, my own death warrant. For I had just become a follower of the Way!

My greatest concern of all, however, at that time, was about my future.

Where did I go from here?

And I had two problems with that.

The first was that the Lord had told me that in Damascus I would be instructed as to what I should do. I had accepted that, but how, practically was that going to happen? All the people with and for whom I had come to Damascus would be incensed at my decision to claim that Jesus Christ was the Messiah, not to mention my desire to serve Him. So they were in no position to tell me. And if they couldn't, who would?

The other concern I had was in relation to a deep desire which I found growing in my breast during those indefinable days of enlightening darkness.

It was quite simple.

I wanted somehow to find, to speak to, to associate myself with, the small group of Christ's followers in the city. It was most peculiar, but the people, whom I had come to Damascus to capture, and flog, and trail in chains back to Jerusalem, were the only people I really wanted to meet at that time.

How, though, could that be managed?

I didn't know who they were, and even if I had known them, they would be scared out of their wits of me and would run from me, rather than coming to me. And I could well understand that.

For three days I struggled with these concerns.

For three days I prayed, not out of a sense of duty or ritual, as I had done so often before, but out of a sense of actually being able to touch God, in a manner I had never known before. It seemed as though He was hearing me, and as I persisted in prolonged and passionate prayer I gradually began to feel that something was going to happen, somehow, but I would have to wait for it. God seemed to be telling me that He would send a message, by a personal messenger, to me sometime. This person would cure me of my blindness, and tell me what to do next. The more I became convinced of this the more I prayed earnestly that it might be soon.

And for three days I neither ate nor drank, and slept only when I became so exhausted by my mental and spiritual struggles that I could do nothing else. It didn't matter to me, either, whether I slept during the night or during the day, for to a newly blinded man, both day and night were the same. My only way of distinguishing between day and night when I was awake was by the voices coming from the front of the house and the constant clamour of activity from the courtyard at the back during the day.

The nights were sessions of usually unshattered silence.

Late in the afternoon of my third day of continuing physical sightlessness but increasing spiritual perception, I was sitting praying to God yet again, for guidance, for direction, for something to happen soon, when I heard an unfamiliar voice in the outer room. Over my period of voluntary isolation I had become able to identify the voices of Judas and his family. This though, was none of them, and it was one I had never heard before.

"Is this the house of Judas?" the as-yet unidentified visitor was enquiring.

"Yes, indeed it is," I could hear my host reply. "And how can I help you?"

"I have been directed to come here," the strong voice continued. "I understand you have a man called Saul of Tarsus staying with you. Is that right?"

"That is right, indeed," Judas replied, sounding astonished. As far as he was aware, very few people, except the guards who had brought me here, and who had by then set off to return to Jerusalem, knew where I was.

"Well could I possibly see him?" the visitor persisted. "I have an important message for him."

"Yes, I suppose you can," Judas conceded, obviously feeling that this visitor meant me no harm. "He is in the back room through there."

If Judas had been astonished at the stranger's request to see me, I was not only astonished at his enquiry after me, but also suspicious of his motive. Was this someone from the High Priest to capture me? Had the temple guards, my travelling companions, betrayed me to the local rabbis? Who was this with 'an important message? Or could this possibly be...? I didn't even dare to hope.

I pulled my only blanket up around my shoulders and cowered in trepidation as I heard the curtain that divided my tiny room off from the rest of the house, being swished aside. This must have been how some of my former victims had felt. Intimidated. Terrified. Apprehensive...

In two steps my visitor had crossed the floor. What was he going to do? Or say? Had he a set of chains? Or a whip? Or, alternatively, could this possibly be God's man? God's messenger? Perhaps it was a local physician to prepare some special potion to give me back my sight? It would be hard to know until he said something. Or did something...

The new arrival in my Straight Street lodging stood there in silence for a few moments, and in that sense of his presence all my doubts were dispelled, and all my anxieties evaporated.

Whoever this was, he was in some inexplicable way, a part of me, and I in that same way, was a part of him. I knew I was safe. There was nothing to fear here.

I felt the gentle touch of his hands on my forehead, and then his fingers slid softly down over my useless eyes. His initial tender touch was reassuring but the first two words he spoke made my heart skip a beat.

"Brother Saul…" he said.

'Brother' Saul!

So that was why I had felt so close to him! That was why I had felt that immediate affinity with this total stranger! He was one of the Damascus disciples of the Nazarene. And he was my 'brother' in Christ!

And the remainder of the message he had brought for me, was no less thrilling than his introduction had been touching.

"Brother Saul, " he said, softly but solemnly, "The Lord, even Jesus, who appeared to you on the road as you were coming here, has sent me that you might have your sight restored, and be filled with the Holy Spirit."

Then an astounding thing happened!

It seemed as though something which was obscuring my vision slowly dropped away, and the blackness was dispelled by a clear shining light, as though some one had opened a curtain across a window in a totally blacked-out room, allowing daylight to penetrate.

I gradually raised my head, and with perfect vision I looked up into the face of the man who had called me 'Brother Saul'. His name he told me was Ananias. He was a Jew but also a believer in Jesus, and God had given him instructions to come to me, complete with precise directions as to where to find me.

The restoration of my sight must have worked a miracle on my tear ducts, too, for I had trouble checking back the tears as I gazed up into the fresh and friendly face of this courageous man, in the simple robe.

If my mission to this city had been permitted to proceed to its intended conclusion this would have been the man I would have most wanted to kill! And he had just five minutes before addressed me as brother Saul'

Wonderful!

The next few hours were wonderful, too.

Ananias passed on to me the solemn message, which God had entrusted to him, and it was humbling, and challenging. Daunting, almost.

It was that I was to be God's special envoy to the Gentile nations, and that I would be called upon to suffer much for His name, from both Jew and Gentile. The dispatch delivered by Ananias proved to be a more detailed reiteration and a definite confirmation of what God had told me, lying mouth down in the choking dust of the Jerusalem Road.

Within days more marvellous things happened.

Ananias encouraged me to be baptised, so I was baptised.

Ananias invited me to meet all the followers of The Way in a small house in an unfrequented side street, so I went to meet them. What an experience that was too! To worship the Lord, collectively, with the complete company whom I had set out to capture!

Then, out of a zeal to begin the task entrusted to me, I went into the synagogue to tell the Jews about what I had just learnt.

Jesus Christ of Nazareth was their Messiah! What a truth! What a revelation!

After a few days in the synagogue at that time, however, I became convinced that I should refrain from public presentation in the meantime.

I realized that I needed to learn more about the salvation provided by God for mankind, through the death of Jesus, 'on a tree' in Jerusalem. I needed to rethink some of the passages of the Sacred Scriptures in light of what I now knew, and above all I needed to commune with God about His precise purpose for my life.

There was just so much to learn!

So after telling Ananias and the others of my hankering to spend quality time alone with God, I left them, promising to return when I considered the time to be right.

It was great to be alone again.

For now I could experience that satisfying sensation of being alone, without feeling lonely.

For days I travelled, constantly conscious of the presence of God all around me, and in continual contact with Him in prayer. I made steady progress southwards, sleeping where I could, and generally avoiding most of the cities and larger towns. The trek was long, but I knew where I wanted to go, and when I arrived at my destination I recognized that it would be an ideal location in which to spend some time in close communion with God, the creator and sustainer of all things.

Almost five weeks of solitary travel had brought me to the Sinai Peninsula. In my student days at Jerusalem I had always promised myself a pilgrimage to that barren place, for so much of the early history of our nation had been enacted there.

That was where Moses had seen the burning bush, where he had been given our Holy Law by direct revelation from God, and where he had spent time in communion with God up amongst the craggy granite peaks.

It was to there also that Elijah had resorted as a depressed and desperate man, in fear for his life, and had been refreshed and renewed at the wells of inspiration.

That place was to become special to me too, for it was in that desert wilderness that God revealed to me much of His programme for my life, and many of the mysteries of His Gospel.

In the very valleys where the manna had fallen, I sat as a student at the feet of my new Master and Teacher, a receptive vessel for the descending droplets of His truth.

In the shadow of Mount Sinai, on whose slopes God had given our law to Moses, I was pressed into pondering the ultimate purpose of the Law.

For years I had sought to attain to righteousness by the meticulous observance of that Law, and just when I thought I was about to achieve it, my entire belief had been shattered to pieces, broken to bits around my feet, like a clay pot dropped on a tiled floor. And now my fanatical fervour for the observance of the law had been replaced by a love, which I couldn't easily explain, for a Man whose memory, message, and claim to be The Messiah I had been endeavouring to eradicate from the face of the earth!

Why had God given the Law to Moses in the first place, if the keeping of it could not bring lasting peace or inner satisfaction? was a question I found myself compelled to contemplate for days. But the answer, when I found it, was simple.

God had furnished us with the law, not to save us, but to highlight our sin, our individual inner inadequacy to dwell in His presence. We would then be forced to turn to Christ, who had offered Himself as a willing sacrifice for sin, and in Him alone we would find salvation.

The Law was a kind of a schoolmaster to direct us to Christ.

I was learning fast.

Those were precious and profitable days in the desert.

During the six months or more that I spent in that remote wilderness I saw very few other people except the odd group of wandering nomads, 'the tent men', as they were called. On the few occasions when these shy people came close enough for me to have any communication with them, I had a chance to practise my skill in tent making, by executing a number of running repairs to their crude brown tents.

Eventually there came a time when I was sure that God was urging me to return to Damascus. He was, I felt, ready to project me from the isolation of my one-to-one contact with Him into the daily challenge of working for Him amongst others. I was to witness to the Jews first, and then on to the Gentiles.

Ananias and the Damascus group were delighted to have me back with them after my return journey, and some of them accompanied me on my first visits to the city synagogues.

If the believers in Damascus were pleased to see me back, the same could certainly not be said for the Jews. Some of them were puzzled at my forsaking of 'the faith of the fathers', as they saw it, and others of them were just downright furious!

And when I began to exercise my right as a rabbi to read from the prophetic scriptures, and then from them teach that Jesus of Nazareth, the crucified carpenter was in fact the Messiah, God's anointed One, they found me just too much to cope with!

The self-satisfied Jews of Damascus became indignant because I had disturbed the deep slumber of their decided opinions. Out of their own scriptures, and using their own time-honoured methods of teaching and learning, I was confounding them by propounding the very same principles that I had found so difficult to refute when disputing with Stephen years before in the synagogue of the Cilicians, back in Jerusalem.

And they didn't like it one bit!

In less than two years they began plotting to kill me. Various of the disciples had heard reliable reports that the city governor had been given authority from King Aretas to mount a round the clock guard on all the city gates, so that if 'Saul of Tarsus' ever tried to escape he could be arrested and killed!

I was, in effect a prisoner in Damascus. And I was also under sentence of death in the city.

What a reversal! What an unbelievable irony!

The zealot who had come to Damascus, some three years before, to take some prisoners, was now a prisoner himself in the city. And the one, who had intended putting the leaders of the hated sect of the Nazarenes to death, was now under sentence of death himself! For no reason other than that he was a leader of the hated sect of the Nazarenes!

The disciples soon became anxious for my safety. They tried to tell me, as though I didn't already know, that the Jewish authorities, once incited, would show no mercy!

The plan they came up with for my escape reminded me of the story of Rahab and the spies from the early books of the sacred writings.

One of the members of that small and faithful group of believers, lived in a house on the city wall and there was a window in the outer wall, above the moat. One particularly black and moonless night, we gathered in that house. Someone had borrowed a big rope basket from one of the street traders, and this basket was secured by a stout rope and pushed out through the window. I then lowered myself out through the window, and holding on to the ledge with my hands, and feeling and fumbling with my feet, I eventually wriggled into the basket. It was scary, that, dangling there in mid-air until I felt the security of the thick base ropes of the bottom of the basket below me, waiting all the time for a shout from a guard from below.

We weren't spotted, however, and after a whispered prayer and a series of tearful goodbyes, I was lowered gently into the moat. A prearranged tug on the rope saw the basket disappear miraculously back in through the window from whence it, and I, had come.

I was alone with my God, my thoughts, and my powerful survival instinct, once again.

As I skirted around the high walls of the silent city in the sheltering blackness, I had only one destination in mind. I had to find the Jerusalem Road.

I had left the Holy City to come to Damascus as Saul the rabbi, Saul the Pharisee, and Saul the exterminator of the Nazarenes.

Now I was beginning my return journey to Jerusalem from Damascus, as 'Brother Saul', member of the sect of the Nazarenes, and commissioned servant of Jesus Christ, the Son of God.

And that could make a difference!

Chapter Five

TO SEE PETER

There was little time to waste.

I had to make the most of the remaining hours of darkness.

It would be important to put as much distance as possible between Damascus and myself before daybreak.

Within an hour of having been dropped off by basket outside the walls I had emerged from an olive grove, and out on to the Jerusalem Road.

I was on my way.

The early slanting shafts of sunlight had just begun to stream across the valley of Damascus when I made my first stop. And I had to stop. I could do nothing else.

It would be totally impossible for me to pass that particular point without stopping for a brief period of reflection and thanksgiving. For I had just come to the spot on the road where I had been so dramatically arrested by a spectacular appearance of the risen Christ, silhouetted in celestial light, about three years before. It was at that place where all my plans for my future had undergone a sensational about turn, and I had suffered a whole personality change too, for I was now an entirely different person. The Saul I had been before that event was not the same Saul as I had since become.

A brief stop was all I dared allow myself, but as I sat below a nearby tree, gazing out at a dusty patch of road, I just thanked God for revealing Himself to me so powerfully, and prayed for guidance in the days ahead.

Then I was off again, travelling southwards.

It was easy to make steady progress, being alone. On this return leg I didn't have to cope with the mood swings of the temperamental temple guards, or listen to the moans of the murmuring muleteers.

All I had to do was walk. And I did, too, for days.

The golden dome of the Temple had always filled me with awe, ever since that first time it had burst upon my sight as a teenager, and when it slid up over the horizon, dazzling in the distance, once more, I knew that I was nearing my journey's end.

As I approached the city gate, however, my mind was jolted back down through the years once more. It was not a pleasant memory this time, though. For as I joined the motley crowd converging on the gate, I was compelled to pause as I passed another spot.

Jagged stones lay in spiked heaps in the sparse and sun-scorched scrub by the roadside.

For a sobering second I seemed to hear a voice call out, "Don't lay this sin to their charge!"

That was followed, in a second sobering second, by a transient vision of a battered and bloodstained body, lying lifeless below a heap of rough and bloodstained stones.

How mightily I had been misled!

Why could I not have been farsighted enough to see the sense of the truth Stephen had tried to tell us from the Scriptures in the Sanhedrin? Instead of that I had been one of the most vociferous in baying for his blood.

How absolutely humiliating, in hindsight!

I felt so sorry that I had been so blinded, but it had all been done because of my beliefs.

My beliefs!

As I mingled with the others, pressing forward into the city I began almost immediately to recall the familiar haunts, and influential people, of my student days.

Hurrying past the towering walls of my old college on the edge of the temple precincts, I thought of Gamaliel, and what he had taught me. My former tutor, whom I had so much respected, would never speak to me again. I knew that. He would 'wash his hands of me', solemnly pondering upon my incomprehensible change of heart.

And what of the high priest, with whose interpretation of the sacred scriptures I now totally disagreed, and whose letters of authority I had long since destroyed? I could scarcely expect him to be either exceptionally enthusiastic or singularly excited on learning of my return to the capital.

The Pharisees, I knew, would be furious, and the rabbis raging.

The Sanhedrin, too, would have a score to settle. They would be seeking to wreak venomous vengeance on this high-profile apostate. They would execute me if they could. Try me as a traitor, and stone me as a Stephen.

I couldn't expect many favours of the Jewish religious establishment.

As I pushed on through the busy and colourful afternoon crowds, not knowing really where to make for, or who to attempt to contact, first, I began to ask myself the question, 'And what am I doing here, anyway?'

If my former associates would all despise me, what had brought me here?

The answer was simple, the reason irresistible.

A burning light of life and love had been kindled deep in the heart of me. I was no longer Saul of Tarsus, expert in the ancient law, and active antagonist of this recent 'Way'. This love for Christ, which had become the driving force in my life, had impelled me imperatively to return to Jerusalem with one express purpose in view.

I had an earnest, fervent desire to meet the original exponents of my newly found faith, those men who had walked with my Lord on earth.

In particular I wanted to see Peter. I longed to hear about the Master from the mouth of one of the foremost of His disciples.

But it would be wonderful, as well, to meet all the Jerusalem based believers, many of whom had walked and talked with Christ, and hear their stories. They would know what He had looked like, what He had said, what He had done, how He had reacted to any and every situation, how He had died on the cross, crucified by the Romans at the whim of the Jews. And all about the resurrection...

That was why I had come.

It would be great to meet them all.

The lonely trek back from Damascus, the rejection by the Jews, and even the uncertainty about my future, would all pale into insignificance, at least temporarily, when I had the privilege of meeting with the Lord's people. These were the very gentle, caring people whose deep love for each other I had witnessed in my misguided malevolent days.

How marvellous it would be to meet with them!

How special it would be to be one of them!

How I anticipated it...!

And what a shock I got!

When I tried to make enquires after the followers of the Way, I drew a blank. Nobody would tell me where they met, and despite repeated requests not one of them would meet me.

How totally sick, and utterly lonely, I felt. I had banked on being with the believers, but now they were refusing to meet me. I felt like an outcast, but all confused. For I had a heart bursting with love for the Lord, a head bursting with direct revelations from the Lord, but I was being deprived of any contact with the friends of the Lord. So I was left without a friend in the world. Except the Lord.

For now the Jews hated me, and the believers were suspicious of me.

A lamb had returned to Jerusalem, they said, but it had the teeth and claws of a wolf.

This yarn about Saul of Tarsus having joined forces with the Nazarenes was obviously nothing more than a cunning and cruel con trick, a reprehensible ruse of their arch-enemy, to draw them out into the open, capture them, torture them, and perhaps even kill them.

There was no way they were falling for that one!

In deep despair I turned to the Lord in prayer, beseeching Him to send someone to me, someone who believed in Him and who would believe me.

And He answered my prayer in the person of Joseph of Cyprus.

It was late one evening when a tall, handsome, bearded man with an earnest face and incredibly convincing, honest eyes, arrived in my lodgings.

This man asked at once if I was Saul of Tarsus. When I told him that I was, he said that he thought he remembered me from of old for he had been a regular visitor to both Tarsus and Jerusalem in his younger day, and my name was well known amongst the Jewish communities, in both those places.

It was my interest in joining the small but scared sect of the Nazarenes which had brought him to see me, he confessed, and for that I was glad.

He said that he had been more widely travelled that most of the Jerusalem believers, and had heard from different sources about how I had been contending for the faith in Damascus, and thus he had come to interview me himself.

It was a bold move on his part, and I appreciated it very much.

We sat talking for hours.

I liked this straight, simple and sincere man, and felt completely at ease telling him of all my experiences. And whether I was apologising for my mistaken persecution of the followers of the faith, relating the saga of my salvation, flat out in the dirt on the road, recalling Divine revelation in isolation in Arabia, or recounting opposition to my teaching in Damascus, I felt it mattered to this gentle Jewish Cypriot. He was one of those great listeners who seemed to be hanging on my every word.

After hearing my story and asking a number of pertinent questions, Joseph of Cyprus seemed convinced that God had indeed saved me by His grace, and earmarked me for His service and volunteered to act as my escort to, and guarantor with, the Apostles.

At last! I was overjoyed!

And what a meeting that turned out to be!

My first encounter was with Peter, James the brother of our Lord, and a few of the other leaders of the group. They were, I suppose understandably, cautious. Not many of them were prepared to commit themselves in the first instance.

Before he addressed them, I realized that the man who had befriended me, whom I knew as Joseph, was known amongst the believers as 'Barnabas', 'the son of consolation'. And I could easily appreciate why! It was no hardship for me to address this gracious, caring man as 'Barnabas' from then on, either!

It was a thrilling, yet touching experience as I stood aside and allowed my trusted and trusting friend to state my case, relating all I had told him, in precise and convincing detail.

I could see that Peter and James were impressed, and after Barnabas had finished speaking they turned their attentions to me and asked me endless questions, which I was only too happy to answer. At least I had been afforded an audience, an opportunity to speak to the elders of the Jerusalem church.

In less than an hour, I knew that I had been accepted amongst them, and Peter offered me the chance to upgrade my accommodation.

I could move in with him!

To see Peter! That's why I had come to Jerusalem, and now God had granted me the opportunity to spend hours, and days, with him.

The next ten days will live in my memory forever.

Peter was usually busy during the day, with many matters concerning the scattered but spreading church, but the nights were particularly precious.

There were so many questions I wanted to ask about my Lord, from someone who had lived in such close communion with Him. Peter told me about how Jesus had called him by the Sea of Galilee, about the transfiguration on the mount, which I was able to compare, in some respects, with my experience on the road, about His teachings, about the crucifixion... There was just so much, and Peter with his bronzed, open face, and alert but impetuous manner, was extremely eager to tell it.

There were nights when the fisherman from Bethsaida, and the tentmaker from Tarsus, the apostle who had been used to see many Jews brought to salvation, and the apostle who had been called to go to the Gentiles with the same message, the one who had been a close companion of Jesus on earth, and one who had seen Jesus appear in a radiant display of heavenly light, had barely time to go to bed at all.

On one or two nights we had to retire because Peter, who was the older and also the physically more active of us during daylight hours, nodded off to sleep through sheer physical exhaustion!

To me, when I had made Peter's acquaintance, I had fulfilled my purpose in going to Jerusalem, but as is often the case with my bountiful Heavenly Father, I was to discover that there were added bonuses to be had in the Holy City as well.

For as I came to be accepted by all the members of the church I realized that there were others who had interesting things to tell, too.

On the nights when I was not having a one-to-one with Peter I visited the house of Mary, the mother of a young man called John Mark, a sincere young follower who was a cousin of my benevolent friend Barnabas. Since it was a larger house than many in the city, Mary's home had become a gathering centre, a focal point, for the steadily growing group.

And in the spacious upper room in that home, by flickering lamplight, and often deep into the sultry night, I heard a number of the believers speak about their experiences during the time of our Lord's ministry amongst them. It was all so instructive, and so exciting. I just couldn't hear enough of it!

One thing annoyed me though. It was a blast from my past, which burned into me like a red-hot needle.

When I enquired as to the whereabouts of the other disciples, such as John, and Philip and Andrew, I was informed that they had fled into remote rural locations because of 'the persecution'. Literally, because of *me*!

As I became increasingly uneasy about this, with my conscience pricking me ceaselessly, I mentioned it one day to Peter who told me not to worry. It must have been, he assured me, in the plan of God, because the apostles had scattered all over the country, preaching the gospel wherever they went. So it ended up that far more people had been saved than would normally have been, had they all remained in Jerusalem!

On reflection, I should have known that anyway, for that was why I had deemed it necessary to set out for Damascus in the first place! An awareness of the plan of God, that Peter had been talking about, for the spread of the gospel, was beginning to dawn upon my eager mind.

With Peter and the others busy during the day I found myself drawn back to the synagogue of the Cilicians. I was exploding with enthusiasm to tell those with whom I had once associated, the truth of what I had just recently discovered and about which I was learning a little more every day.

Jesus Christ, the carpenter of Nazareth, who had taught in the temple in this city, and who had been crucified as a criminal outside this city, is alive, and what is more, He is the Messiah, the Promised and Anointed One of God.

So in the very synagogue where I had so vehemently opposed Stephen, I began preaching the faith, which I had once sought to destroy, amongst people whom I had once known as allies, but who were now bitter enemies.

Although they didn't say much about it, for they understood my unmistakeable passion for telling others of my Lord, I gathered from the attitude of Peter and James, and to a certain extent, too, even Barnabas, that they considered my action just a fraction foolhardy.

And within days they had heard that the Jews were plotting to kill me again.

I had just met the Saviour three years before, and now I had the death squads after me for the second time in three months! The hunter had become the hunted once more.

God had placed me on the receiving end yet another time. This was merely stage two of my introductory course into what I was going to be called upon to suffer for His Name.

One afternoon I had gone up to the temple at the hour of prayer, and was spending some time in silent meditation. Although increasingly conscious of the threat to my life, I knew the Jews would not carry out their devious designs in the temple. It would be wrong to defile the Holy Place with the blood of a heretic. They would have to assassinate me somewhere else.

As I prayed in the cool of the temple in the heat of the afternoon, I fell into a trance and the Lord appeared to me, in person, in a vision. I could not mistake His presence, but I was not prepared initially for the message He had come to convey.

"Hurry up, Saul, you must leave Jerusalem at once!" He told me. "These Jews will not believe what you are telling them about Me."

"But, Lord, they must, they should…" I began to protest. "These people here know me. They know how I persecuted the believers and they even know that when Stephen, your martyr, was killed, I was there, consenting to his killing, and guarding the clothes of the killers. Lord they are bound to have seen the change in my life! They are bound to recognize what faith in You has done for me!"

The Master was patient, but firm.

"No, Saul," He persisted. "You must leave this city at once. I am sending you out from here to work amongst the Gentiles. Now, go. Leave. Get out!"

I must have sounded like a slow learner to my Lord. That was the *third* time He had told me that my work would be amongst the Gentiles, and still I was trying to insist upon staying in Jerusalem! How stubborn of me, but my years of rabbinical involvement and my affection for the Holy City were proving hard to shake off, difficult to desert.

When I told Peter about the vision he made immediate arrangements to have me escorted safely out of the city, and on towards the eventual fulfilment of my God-appointed goal. The Gentiles.

Yet another flight by night saw me leave Jerusalem with a small but dependable group of men from the city church, and set out down the Roman road over the hillsides and along the bed of the steep winding valleys to the plain by the Great Sea.

At last we came within sight of the newly built palace, stadium and hippodrome of the coastal town of Caesarea. One of my attendants told me that Herod the Great had employed thousands of slaves in the construction of those magnificent edifices.

We had no time to ponder on architectural splendour, however, as we pushed purposefully through the streets of the town, and down to the busy harbour.

A few urgent enquiries amongst the sailors lounging about in the sunshine, waiting for the slaves to load up their ships, soon revealed that a vessel was due to sail for my home city of Tarsus at daybreak next morning, calling at Seleucia, the port of Antioch in Syria, on the way.

As the ship pulled out of the harbour that next morning I stood and waved to the small band of believers who had brought me so faithfully thus far, until they eventually turned to retrace their steps to the capital.

Then I took a seat, and as the oars, pulled by the galley slaves, rose and fell, flashed and glinted, in the early morning sunlight I watched them, transfixed, looking but not seeing, trying to make sense of what was going to happen to me now.

I had left Jerusalem, the city where I had been educated in the ancient law, and the city where my Lord had been rejected by the exponents of that very same law, and was heading for Tarsus where I had been born, and where my Lord was unknown

And Tarsus was a *Gentile* city.

Was that where I was to begin my life's work? I wondered.

And if it was, how would the citizens of that prosperous university town react to the message of my Saviour's love?

Time would tell.

Chapter Six

I HAVE BEEN LOOKING
FOR YOU

Tarsus had changed when I returned to it.

Or perhaps it was just me. It could have been that since the former citizen had changed he felt that his former city had changed, too.

Somehow I sensed that I didn't belong there any more.

For although the current of my life was now proceeding in peaceful flow, I found myself beset by an always tugging undercurrent of restlessness, for I believed that my home city was not to be my final destination. I wasn't going to end my days there. God was telling me that I would have other places to go, and other functions to fulfil, for Him. In the meantime, however, since I didn't know where they were, or what they were, I couldn't act upon them.

Last time I had left Tarsus, it had been as Saul the fanatical Pharisee, prepared to wipe the Way from the face of the earth. And when I had returned it had been as a follower of the Nazarene, prepared to promote the Way across the face of the earth, and to the ends of the earth.

Small wonder that my father, the fervent Pharisee, was furious. What a shock to him! And what an affront to the family!

His son, for whom he had such high hopes, had become a traitor to the ancestral faith. After a few sessions of acrimonious debate, he disowned me completely, having taken great pains to inform me that he was cutting me off from my 'inheritance'.

When I chose to visit my home synagogue and attempted to present the true interpretation of the scriptures I had so diligently learnt there as a boy, I met with some fierce opposition. The rabbis, many of whom I knew, and with whom I had often discussed the sacred writings ever so seriously, now disputed my every word, ever so sarcastically.

I was not deterred, however.

Despite the setbacks, there were some signs of encouragement.

God had indicated to me, no less than three times, that I was to become His herald to the Gentiles. So I did two things.

With my constantly enquiring mind I began to probe into the literature and philosophy of the Greeks. Tarsus was a university city and a centre for Greek learning and culture, but I had never been exposed, as a dedicated Jewish boy, from a dedicated Jewish family, to such 'heathen' influences. Now I realized that a working knowledge of Gentile beliefs would eventually aid me in reaching Gentiles for Jesus. If I could understand where they were coming from, then I could all the more effectively point them to my Lord, the Creator of mankind who became the crucified and resurrected Christ. I could prove conclusively from my own experience that faith in Him far transcended formal tradition, and I wanted to be in a position to prove that it was far superior to either a vague, intellectual pantheism or a passionate, idol-worshipping paganism, as well.

And that became my second, and infinitely more important pursuit. To my father's absolute disgust, when I wasn't making tents to make a living, I began making initially short, and then increasingly longer, trips into the towns and villages of Syria and Cilicia, making known the good news of salvation through faith in Jesus Christ, to any and all who would listen. 'Propounding his heresy to heathens', was how my father chose to describe it.

Eventually I began to see some sprouting seeds of blessing. A few became convinced and then became disciples, eagerly embracing the Way.

Nor did my Lord leave me alone.

On long arduous tent-making days, when I had to work to buy bread, or on long and tiring travelling days, when I had to walk for many a mile between my talking and teaching destinations, I wondered about my life's ultimate purpose. And that was when He appeared occasionally to reassure me, by a direct disclosure of Himself.

On one such occasion, about six years after my return to Tarsus, I experienced an amazing out of the body, substantially supernatural sensation. That night I was enraptured, and spirited away from this earth and everything earthly, to what could only have been the paradise of God, where I saw scenes of unbelievable beauty and glory and heard sounds of unbelievable melody and majesty.

What happened that night I am still at a loss to explain, nor can I find the words to even begin to express!

But such visions kept me focused.

They increased my conviction that I was standing on the threshold of something big for God, but I had no idea what it was. It felt as though I was impatiently drawing patterns in the dust outside the door of the house of Tremendous Opportunity, while eagerly awaiting the master's invitation to enter...

Then one day the call came.

I had just returned less than two days from one of my walking, talking, and preaching trips when a man I knew met me in the street.

"Did you see the stranger who was looking for you, Saul?" he enquired.

"No, I didn't," I replied, my curiosity aroused. "Who was it?"

"Oh, I don't know," the man went on. "He said he would keep coming back to your house until he found you."

Now I was really puzzled. Who could be looking for me? It would hardly be any of my relatives for I scarcely saw any of them now except my sister who called very rarely, and anyway this had been a man. Nor could it have been someone from the Jewish religious tradition, for they had long since given up on me, and ignored me completely.

It was early next morning before the problem was solved, and my curiosity satisfied.

I had just left the door of the house where I was lodging to walk up to the market place when I heard a voice call me from the opposite direction. It sounded familiar, and when I turned quickly I saw someone breaking into a run, his robes flapping around him, to come to me.

It was Barnabas!

On reaching the spot were I stood momentarily mesmerised he half-smothered me in a warm embrace and exclaimed, "Oh Saul, I have been looking for you all over this city! Lovely to see you again!"

"It's great to see you, too!" I replied meaning every word of it, for I was very fond of this open, honest big man. "But what are you doing here?"

"What am I doing here?" he repeated my question with a short laugh. "I have already told you that. I am looking for you! That's what I am doing here!"

"I am delighted to see you again, Barnabas." I repeated. "But is there any particular reason why you are looking for me?"

"Yes, Saul, there is a very important and specific reason why I have come to try and track you down. Is there anywhere that we can sit and have a talk?" my trusted friend enquired.

"Let us go back to my room," I suggested. "Then we can talk as long as we like."

When we had settled ourselves in comfortable positions Barnabas revealed the purpose of his mission.

It was, he soon explained, all to do with what was happening across in Antioch in Syria. Apparently some travelling preachers from Cyprus and Cyrene had made bold there, more that a year before, and had begun to teach about Jesus and The Way to the Greeks in that huge cosmopolitan city.

And they had received it gladly!

When the apostles in Jerusalem heard of this they had dispatched Barnabas to review the situation. They were anxious to establish if this was a work of God or not, or just another spurious sect, eager to dabble in some hitherto untried philosophy.

What Barnabas had seen had obviously inspired him. For he was full of it.

"Saul, I believe that this is a manifestation of the purposes of God, a real work of the Holy Spirit. There seem to be people of all nationalities and backgrounds joining us every week! This is surely the beginning of something marvellous," he kept stressing.

Then, when he felt that he had obviously said enough to impress me too, and that hadn't proved difficult, for his ardour was infectious, he came to the simple reason for his visit.

"Saul, I want you to come back with me and share in that work. There are not enough of us there to cope with all that needs to be done. We need help urgently," he stated simply. " And I believe that you are the man for the job, for at least two reasons."

Now I knew the purpose of this welcome but unexpected visit.

Barnabas had spelt it out quite clearly.

Could this be my big break for God? I wondered.

"What would those reasons be, Barnabas?" I asked, after a thoughtful pause, not wishing to commit myself too readily. "I mean, why me? What about Peter or John or James, or some of the leaders in Jerusalem?"

"Saul, this is not a work for native Jews like Peter, or any of those others you have named," Barnabas explained patiently. "This work requires a younger man, and certainly somebody with a more brilliant brain than mine. It needs to be someone passionately in love with our Lord, someone well versed in the Jewish scriptures but also conversant with Greek culture. And if that someone just happened to be a Roman citizen, too, that could prove nothing but a bonus in multicultural Antioch!"

I had to smile. Barnabas was such an intrinsically good man. There was no jealousy about him, just sincerity. And he must have spent some time working out his arguments.

His second reason was even more convincing than the first, however, and more difficult to disregard, as he continued speaking, not even pausing to allow me a chance to respond.

"Remember Jerusalem, Saul?" he enquired, looking me straight in the eye. "Remember your vision? Remember what the Lord told you then? Was it not that He was sending you out to be His messenger to the Gentiles?"

"Yes," I agreed, but not admitting to having wondered about it for some time. "That was it."

"Well the work of God amongst the Gentiles is exploding into life in Antioch, Saul. It is unbelievable what is happening over there! Greeks and Romans are giving up idol worship and emperor worship to worship the Lord. Will you come and help us?"

Barnabas was so persuasive, and I felt the leading of the Lord in it.

This must have been what I was waiting for.

"I will," I replied at once.

Chapter Seven

CHRISTIANS

As we crossed the mighty bridge, that carried the Roman road over the River Orontes on its majestic arches and pressed forward into the busy city of Antioch, I was convinced that a new age and stage in my life had begun.

It seemed that I had somewhere abandoned the trappings of my Jewish upbringing.

As a boy I had approached Jerusalem in the company of my father.

Now, as a man, I was approaching Antioch, the third largest city in the Roman Empire, next only to Rome and Alexandria, in the company of my close friend, Barnabas.

I had gone to Jerusalem to become proficient in the Law and the Prophets.

Now I had arrived in Antioch, just itching to begin unfolding the fulfilment of the Law and the Prophets, in the person of the crucified Christ.

As we passed through the gate into the city I was immediately impressed by the stately splendour of the Street of the Colonnades. I strained to see the far end of it but couldn't, for it was four miles long and the white marble of its central paving stones, which were dazzling in the early afternoon sun, just disappeared into a long white streak in the hazy distance. Covered walkways, or colonnades, protected the rows of shops and dwellings on either side of the paved street, from the sun and the rain. The ambling shoppers could buy a vast array of goods from the multitude of shops and stalls that were laid out along the length of that striking street, at their leisure and in comfort, whatever the weather.

I was even more impressed when Barnabas told me that I would soon see that the shoppers even thronged the street at night, for there was late night shopping in Antioch, most nights of the week. The colonnades, he informed me, were illuminated every evening to permit the wealthy residents of that magnificent city to parade themselves, both night and day.

And what a mixture those citizens were.

As we tramped along I began to think that in the course of my first ten minutes in Antioch I must have looked into the face of a representative from every known nation on the earth!

There were sturdy, stocky Roman soldiers, bargaining Greek merchants, olive-faced, black-haired Jews, bronzed and weather-beaten Arabs from the desert regions, and coloured people seemed to come from every country under the sun.

'I will send you to the Gentiles', was what God had told me.

It looked as though 'Antioch the Beautiful, 'the Heathen Queen', would be as good a place as any to start.

I had trouble keeping pace with Barnabas. He knew the city well, and strode through the covered walkways, on his long legs. He seemed possessed with a single purpose and the multinational nature of the citizens of this vast city of half a million people didn't seem to hold the same fascination for him as it did for me.

After we had passed a series of fountains and statues, and some gardens ablaze with bloom, we reached a side street where Barnabas turned off.

He told me that it was called Singon Street, and that's where he lodged, in a large house with a room big enough to double as a meeting place for the church.

When we entered that house a number of the believers were waiting for us. How they knew we were coming I could not quite understand, but they welcomed Barnabas warmly.

And then he, in turn, introduced me to them, every bit as warmly.

"This is Saul, the Tarsian," he said. "He is a learned man, a former opponent, but now an able exponent of The Way."

Then as we walked around, he presented some of the men to me, one by one. There was a foster-brother of Herod's, two coloured men, and a younger man with a sharp intelligent look about him that I liked. He was called Titus, the Greek.

It was both a thrill and a humbling experience to meet them all. It was soul-stirring to hear of the marvellous manner in which the Spirit of God had moved in that city over the past few years. And it was an added joy to witness the fervour with which they reported to Barnabas of all the spiritual goings-on within the church and the city, since he had left to travel to Tarsus to look for me.

The humbling bit came with the calm assurance that at last I was where I felt God wanted me to be, a small part of a mighty master plan, to spread the gospel of Jesus Christ to the Gentile nations. The cordial reception I was accorded by the brethren helped me to feel at home straight away. It was strange how I had always believed that Tarsus was not to be my final destination, or the springboard for my God-appointed service.

Now, though, in this seemingly godless, totally pleasure-ridden city, I knew that I had arrived!

"We are so pleased to have you with us, Saul," Simeon, who was an African, said, presuming to speak for all the believers. " Barnabas has told us your story, how that the Lord appeared to you on the road outside Damascus, and many of the things that have happened to you since. We have heard recently about your preaching in Cilicia, and how that God has been blessing you in your work. You will be a great help to us here in the city, we are sure."

I thanked him, and said that I hoped that with the help of God we could all be helpers together.

And that first year in Antioch proved to be one of the happiest, and also most productive of my life in the service of God.

The city was ripe for the Gospel.

There were so many disillusioned people in Antioch.

There were rich people, in search of satisfaction which had so far eluded them in a life of shallow, sensual pleasure.

There were people who worshipped strange gods, and others who were seeking a god to worship. Some of these interested individuals began stopping in the market place as we preached, and then came along to ask questions and hear more, when we gathered in Singon Street.

And there were thousands of slaves, of all nationalities, who desperately craved a purpose in life, something to live for beyond endless, thankless labour.

As we spread the message of peace and satisfaction, of the forgiveness of sins through the grace of God and the death and resurrection of Christ, many believed.

The brethren were very thankful to God for this movement of salvation across almost every racial, religious and cultural divide.

Many from Antioch were turning to Christ.

And many of those new converts began talking about Christ, and what faith in Him meant to them, to virtually everyone they met.

This widespread witness led to us being given a wonderful nickname.

"Have you heard what they are calling us?" one of our brethren asked one evening as we met. I gathered by his expression that he wasn't quite sure whether we would be pleased or grieved at what he had to report.

"Yes," someone else replied, "I have heard it too."

"Well what is it?" Barnabas enquired. "Come on, tell us."

The poets, philosophers and intellectual idlers of Antioch were well-known for their propensity to accord nicknames, many of which were certainly less than flattering, to any new individual of rank who arrived in the city, or as in our case, any new movement or belief which appeared in the city.

So we all wanted to know what they were calling us.

In response to the request of Barnabas, the first man to have mentioned the matter spoke again.

"They are calling us Christians!" he announced.

There was silence for a moment or two when everyone contemplated our recently acquired collective nickname.

"I have to say, I would have no objections to that," someone commented at length. And one by one others agreed.

It was funny because for a few minutes the room was full of the whispered word.

"Christian, Christian, Christian, Christian…" came drifting across from all quarters. There was a soothing freshness about it, like the rustling of a light wind in the leaves of the plane trees that lined the banks of the Orontes.

"We should really count it a privilege, and a challenge, to take upon ourselves the name of Christ," Barnabas remarked at length.

Something else had struck me about the name as I thought about it, and listened to the comments of others.

"You know this is a most appropriate name," I commented at length. "For it is a Greek word, Christ, which means the Anointed One, or to Jewish thinking The Messiah, with a Roman suffix, 'ian'. We are not Syrian, or Alexandrian, or Grecian, or Herodian, but CHRISTian!"

I could see nods of approval, so I continued the theme. For a further, even far more exciting thought had come to me. "With a Greek name, which has a Hebrew meaning, and a Latin ending, we are set to go into all the world and preach the Gospel. To be called Christians can only be good for us!"

Everyone agreed. They would count it an honour, to be called by the name of Christ, while feeling all the more keenly the responsibility which it placed upon them. And that was to portray the nature of Christ.

And so it was that the name which had been given in jest, we accepted with joy.

The name which had been given as a stigma, we accepted as a distinction.

We were now happy to be known as Christians.

And as a group of Christians we grew.

Many more seemed to be added to the church every month. It was a period of real blessing.

Then one day there arrived amongst us a travel-weary group of believers from Jerusalem. Having heard continuing reports of a mighty movement of God at Antioch they had come to bring us greetings from the church in the Holy City, and one of them, a prophet named Agabus, startled us with the prediction that a time of famine was set to come upon Judea, and that many of the poor believers would find life difficult.

I knew from my past associations with the Temple that a fund was available for use in times of hardship, and was distributed in the form of *chaluka,* or alms. I knew also, however, of the allegations of corruption by the priests, in the distribution of this aid, so I could be fairly confident that if they couldn't be trusted to care for their followers in a fair and even-handed way, their enemies, whom they still referred to disparagingly as 'the sect of the Nazarenes', could expect little in the way of aid from the establishment.

The predictions of a famine, and the probability of tough times ahead for the Jerusalem church, pierced like a flaming arrow into my heart.

This was not the first time that things had been tough for the church at Jerusalem. And I had been the root cause of the first, and to date the worst, of their troubles.

We would have to do something to help the beleaguered poor. Kind-hearted Barnabas, who had earlier sold off much of his own property in Cyprus for the common good, helped me organize an Emergency Aid programme.

The Christians in Antioch responded immediately and liberally to our appeals for funds. They were only too willing to share some of what they had, however little, with their counterparts in Jerusalem, who had even less.

As the amount of money collected began to accumulate, week-by-week, I witnessed a miracle of the grace of God grow before my eyes.

Our Lord had been crucified in Jerusalem, had risen from the dead in Jerusalem, and had left to return to heaven, from outside Jerusalem.

Before He left, however, Peter told me that He had commanded the little fearful band of faithful followers to go into all the world and make disciples of all nations. He had given me more or less the same command on the Damascus road.

And now the first fruits of that harvest were ready for reaping!

The focus of the church had moved north from Jewish Jerusalem to multiracial Antioch, and now an enthusiastic band of disciples from all nations was collecting, out of a genuine love for their Lord and their fellow-believers, to supply a famine relief package to the band of still fearful followers in Jerusalem!

Amazing!

I often felt like weeping when I let my mind wander all over the wonder of it!

When a sizeable fund had been accumulated we went out amongst the myriad of merchants in Antioch to spend it on food for the struggling saints in Jerusalem. It would be pointless bringing them money to buy corn when there was no corn to be bought. We knew that our aid would have to extend beyond the supply of the funds to the supply of the food.

Within weeks we had built up a small store of sacks of corn from Egypt, cases of dried fruit from Greece and packs of figs from Cyprus. Then, when we had managed to hire a mule train to transport all the sacks and packs we were ready to set off southwards.

The leaders of the church at Antioch agreed with our suggestion that it would be a good idea to invite young Titus to accompany us. This would serve a dual purpose.

The first benefit of bringing him along could be a very practical one. Since he was fit and strong he could help with all the loading and unloading which would be necessary in the distribution of our cargo.

In addition, however, his presence would also provide a very useful demonstration of a truth which some of the believers in Jerusalem were finding really difficult to accept. That was that the salvation of God had broken through the boundaries of Judaism, and that one did not need to be, or become, a Jew, to become a Christian.

Our arrival in Jerusalem after the slow trek south with a number of mules all laden with supplies was greeted with great pleasure and heartfelt gratitude. It was not until we arrived at our destination that we were able to appreciate the serious nature of the situation in the capital. Many of our friends were finding it extremely difficult to obtain enough food to even provide their families with one good meal per day.

We stayed with Mary, who was a much thinner lady than I had remembered from eight or so years before, but still every bit as much in love with her Lord as she had been then. Hardship hadn't altered that in any way.

The food distribution was an inspiring experience for a number of reasons. Not only did it perform the very practical function of providing for the daily needs of a church community on the verge of starvation, but it also allowed us the opportunity to bring to them the greetings of the growing church in Antioch. Barnabas and I recognised that the emergency food supply from the flourishing church, most of whom were Gentile 'Christians', to the afflicted church, most of whom were Jewish 'followers of the Way', did more to establish a bond of love between them than a year's teaching and preaching could have done.

Our visit also allowed the Jerusalem believers to bring us up to date on what had been happening in the city in recent days.

It would appear that Herod had decided for some reason to hound them mercilessly, just as I had once done. He had ordered the execution of James, the brother of John and had thrown Peter into prison. God had intervened, though, in a miraculous way, both in the release of Peter and the judgement of Herod. He had sent an earthquake and Peter was able to walk out of prison to a prayer meeting, and Herod had suffered an unexpected and agonising death.

All that, with a famine to follow, had left the believers shaken but not shattered, bent but not broken.

Their faith in God was both sure and steadfast. And the sense of the continuing power and presence of the Lord amongst them was unbelievable.

When all the food that we had brought with us had been satisfactorily distributed and most gratefully received, we decided that it was time to return to Antioch. There was still so much to be done up there. We felt that we had only so far seen the first small and tender pickings of a potentially abundant harvest. God was still set to work wonders amongst the Gentile nations. Peter and the other apostles were ideally equipped to care for the little church in Jerusalem.

We had better return to our operational base.

Although it had only taken three of us to supervise the transportation of the Aid from Antioch to Jerusalem, four set out on the return journey.

During our days with Mary we had come to know John Mark, her son, very well. Although quite a bit younger, John Mark was Barnabas' cousin, and he seemed very interested in the work of the Lord, and kept bombarding us with questions about Antioch and the church there. Although still little more than a boy at the time, Mark had been in the Holy City during the crucifixion and resurrection, and Mary told us that he had been plying Peter with questions too about the bits he didn't already know.

His eager brain seemed ever anxious to learn more and more about the life of our Lord and the expanding work of the church.

Since Peter was out of the city, temporarily, on a visit elsewhere at that time, and John Mark had such a good rapport with his big, in every way, cousin Barnabas, Mary said that she would be happy if her son could join us, perhaps even for a short time.

That to me, sounded like a good idea.

I liked the lad, with his transparent love for his Lord and His people. He was the sort of person whom I felt could be used of God in years to come, if exposed to the proper training.

And it would, too, like the food aid programme, be good for community relations between the churches.

We had brought Titus the Greek, from Antioch to Jerusalem, to introduce him there.

Now we had grasped the opportunity to bring John Mark the Jew, from Jerusalem to Antioch, to introduce him there.

Titus and Mark were both intelligent young men from totally different racial and religious backgrounds, but they had one fantastic factor in common. And that was their faith in Jesus Christ.

It was thrilling for both Barnabas and me to witness them get to know one another, and hear them share their many and varied experiences of God and His grace, as we trudged northwards towards Antioch.

They were both so much in love with Christ.

There could be no doubt about it.

They were genuine *Christians.*

Chapter Eight

SAUL ... OR IS IT PAUL?

On my return to Antioch I found it hard to settle.

Having spent just over a year there, I had witnessed the gradual growth of the church in the city, not only in numbers but also in the knowledge of and dedication to God. When I had arrived there from Tarsus they had been right in the middle of an infancy of rapid development, but now they had advanced to an admirable maturity.

Since I had been through so much with Barnabas I suggested to him one day that perhaps the time was ripe for the church at Antioch to extend its sphere of influence. Could we perchance even ponder the possibility of sending someone out to somewhere else, in much the same way as a few of the early disciples from Cyprus had come to that city some years before?

I was intrigued to discover that he had been thinking much along the same lines. And when we mooted the idea amongst the other leaders in the church there it seemed that the possibility of such a venture for God had been at least considered by them as well. Although they didn't come out and say it in so many words they recognized that the work of God had progressed apace in the city when we had been absent in Jerusalem, and now the three who left to carry out the Alms from Antioch operation had returned as four! It seemed selfish somehow to hoard such an embarrassment of spiritual wealth in Antioch when there were hundreds of cities throughout the Empire where the name of Christ had never once been proclaimed, and hundreds of thousands of people who had never come into contact with a Christian.

We decided to give the matter some prolonged and prayerful consideration. And within a matter of weeks a decision was reached.

All our fellow-believers were firmly convinced that the Holy Spirit was indicating that Barnabas and I should be set apart for the work of God, with the specific aim of carrying the message of the crucified and risen Saviour to those who were still stumbling about in the darkness of idolatry or seeking satisfaction in the philosophical emptiness of heathendom.

A time of prayer and fasting was called amongst the members of the church and this served to confirm that everyone felt that this was the proper course of action, under the guidance of God.

This decision was not taken lightly, and in fact some expressed a heartfelt concern that in losing Barnabas they would lose one of their most gracious and highly respected leaders, and if I went as well they would lose one of their 'most knowledgeable teachers'. They said it, not me.

However, since all our members were eager to see the Gospel spread and admitted that their reasons for wanting to keep the two of us in Antioch were also the reasons which pointed to the fact that we should be the pair to go, they arranged a further period of special prayer for blessing on the enterprise. Then the other leaders of the church, with whom we had worked so closely, laid hands upon us and collectively commended us to the service of God.

This proved a particularly moving experience for me.

When lying flat on my face in the dust outside Damascus, when camping in the wilderness of Sinai, and when praying in the temple at Jerusalem, God had told me that I would be his chosen instrument to carry the message of the Gospel of Jesus Christ to the Gentile nations. And now, my brethren, directed by the Spirit of God, had confirmed that choice.

When it was accepted that Barnabas and I should leave Antioch to further the mission of making disciples of all nations, we were immediately faced with the problem of where to begin. What, we wondered, should be our first port of call?

That issue proved simpler than expected to resolve.

Since Barnabas was from Cyprus and had many contacts there, we decided that the fruitful island would be an ideal place to begin. Many traders crossed to Antioch from there, and its north-eastern port of Salamis was just seventy miles, or an easy day's sail with a fair wind, from Seleucia,

A further factor in favour of starting in Cyprus was that it had a very large Jewish settlement. Many Jews had migrated to the island to work in the vineyards, on the fruit plantations, and in the copper mines which had been leased to Herod the Great from the Roman Emperor.

Although our aim was to reach the Gentile nations with the message of life and salvation, yet probably because of my background and ingrained knowledge of the law and the prophets, I always relished the opportunity to speak in a synagogue. As a trained rabbi I felt comfortable with the system in the synagogue, and would invariably be invited to speak there.

It was with a mixture of emotions that we set sail early one morning. We had agreed to bring John Mark with us to help arrange a number of the practicalities of the trip to allow us to concentrate on the more important spiritual matters, so the three of us boarded the small trading ship with our sense of adventure tinged with a sense of apprehension.

A small group had accompanied us down from the city of Antioch to the port of Seleucia to see us off, and assembled on the pier before we left. They stood watching as the boat slid out of the harbour and set off across the shimmering waters of the Great Sea.

When they vanished from our view all three of us turned to face the prow. Out ahead in the distance the mountains which formed the backbone of Cyprus were beginning to poke through the morning mist. There was something awesome but alluring about their veiled beauty.

And that was how I felt.

There was something daunting about the unknown challenge ahead, but an assuring serenity in knowing that what I was doing was what God had planned for me, years ago, from before I was born, perhaps.

The journey passed quickly and on our first Sabbath ashore in Salamis we went into a synagogue and began to teach. Then a few Sabbaths later we entered another one. And so we went around all the synagogues in that town. Barnabas was well known by some on the island and we soon fell into a pattern for our synagogue presentations. He spoke a few words of greeting, outlined our mission, and then when he had introduced me I proceeded to use a reading or readings from the sacred scriptures to teach the truth that the prophecy of the Promised One had been fulfilled in the person of our Lord Jesus Christ.

After some time in the busy seaport of Salamis, we travelled westwards across the island, speaking in synagogues on the Sabbath, and to the scattered Jewish communities, where and when we found them, and to as many of the islanders, both Greek and Roman, as would listen.

It was only after we had reached the town of Paphos, however, on the southwestern seaboard, that we had our first really fruitful encounter for God.

We had only been in the town about three weeks, teaching in the synagogue, and speaking to many in the marketplace when we received an invitation to present ourselves in the court of the Roman proconsul of the island. And an invitation to appear before a Roman ruler was treated as a command by a Roman citizen, but it was a command that Barnabas and I were more than happy to obey.

When we arrived at the proconsul's residence we were led through courtyards where fountains sparkled in the sunshine, to keep the air cool, right into the presence of Sergius Paulus, the governor, himself.

Whether he found Paphos rather dull and dozy after the constant buzz of activity in Rome and had summoned us to help pass yet another hot and sleepy afternoon, or whether he was genuinely interested in what he had heard about us, we had no way of knowing.

Perhaps it was a blend of both.

But whatever the reason, when we were ushered into the marble hall where he sat, surrounded by courtiers with a wide range of responsibilities, Sergius Paulus welcomed us courteously. One of his retinue was introduced as Bar-Jesus, or son of Jesus, an astrologer. I knew that Gentile rulers, not knowing the God whom I had come to know, often consulted such men before making decisions on important matters. And I was also convinced that many of them were crooks and charlatans.

For some strange reason I didn't trust this Bar-Jesus, with his long colourful clothes and dangling charms.

After the formal welcome, the proconsul asked us the normal question usually put to a court visitor.

"What is your name, and from what country do you come?" he enquired.

In our sessions in the synagogues Barnabas had always dealt with the preliminaries, but this was different. We were not in a synagogue now. We were in the palace of a Roman proconsul, being addressed in Greek.

It seemed the most natural thing in the world then, since I was a Roman citizen, and a more fluent Greek speaker, that I should take the leading role in this situation.

From childhood, because of my dual citizenship, and also because of the multiracial composition of my home city, Tarsus, I had been given two names, my Jewish name of Saul, and its Roman equivalent, Paul.

So when asked my identity in a Roman court it came almost as second nature to me to use my Roman name.

"My name is Paul, and I am a Roman citizen, from Tarsus in Cilicia," I informed him.

I could see that Sergius Paulus, being a Roman of the House Of Paulli himself, appeared interested.

"And why have you come to Cyprus? What is this doctrine which they tell me you are teaching in the town?" he appeared anxious to know.

That was just what I had been waiting for! What an opportunity! An invitation to present the truth about God, and his Son, in the presence of a Roman ruler.

I knew however that I could not begin with this man, telling him about the Jewish Messiah. A different approach was called for. So I began by presenting God as the Supreme Power, the Creator of all things who through His Son Jesus had the power to free us from the darkness of evil by which we were surrounded and in which we were ensnared in this world. If we trusted in Him, he could forgive us our sins, release us from the bondage of darkness and bring us into an entirely different kingdom of light and love.

As I continued speaking I could see that Bar-Jesus, the astrologer, or Elymas, the Wise, to use the Arabic named he had adopted, was becoming increasingly restless. He had been glancing from me to his master, back and forward, back and forward. And as he saw Sergius Paulus become more engrossed in what I was saying, he became more agitated. He was probably fearing for his job! He was on easy money and enjoyed a lovely lazy lifestyle there in the palace at Paphos!

Eventually he could bear it no longer, and began to contradict me.

If his master believed what I was setting forth, he knew he was in big trouble, so he probably decided to go on the offensive.

His first few interjections I chose to ignore.

This he obviously found galling.

Then, as he persisted, I began countering his angry arguments by putting forward ordered arguments of my own. Although a totally non-Jewish debate, my teenage training in the House of Interpretation stood me in good stead there. 'Keep your head and present your point', was what Gamaliel had always told us.

There came a time when I was forced to ignore that good advice, however. I could see that Satan was using this plausible phoney to thwart the purposes of God.

Switching my attention from the proconsul for a moment I fixed my gaze on the subtle sorcerer, and unable to resist the temptation to use a word play on his name, I announced sternly, "You son of the devil, you enemy of all that is good, you cunning cheat, are you never going to stop twisting the straight ways of the Lord? Beware, for the hand of God will strike you blind so that you won't be able to see the sun, or even distinguish day from night for a day or two!"

As I turned to continue addressing the island's governor, I was aware that my prediction as to the fate of the fortune-teller had already begun to be fulfilled.

His eyes darted quickly from one person to another in the assembled group, and then he shuffled out of his position in the line of courtiers to attempt to look past us and out to the courtyard beyond. Then he put his hands up over his eyes and rapidly removed them again like a child playing peek-a-boo.

I had already resumed speaking to the proconsul for I had just reached the point where I had begun outlining God's plan for the world in the Person of His Son, before I had to leave off to confront the con-man, so I paid little attention to his antics.

My discourse was then interrupted once more by a piercing cry of agonized realization.

"Help me! Please help me! I'm going blind! I can't SEE!"

A servant moved swiftly across to the panic-stricken impostor, and taking him gently by the hand led him out a back door from the marbled hall where we had gathered.

His plight reminded me so much of my entry into Damascus that day so many years before, a broken man, led by a servant. The only difference between him and me was that although I had lost my sight I had found pervading peace. He had lost his sight and had been seized by increasing panic.

The last words we heard from him, as his frantic yells became like little more than the wailing of a distant wind, were, "Beware of those men! They have more power than I ever had! Help me! Please help me! I can't see! Please help…"

He was right, in a way.

We had more power than he had ever had, it was true, but it was not our power. It came alone from God.

And it was also through the power of God, which we had been trying to explain in our speech to the proconsul, and which God had chosen to demonstrate in the temporary blinding of Bar-Jesus, a true son of Satan, that Sergius Paulus became a believer.

The conversion of the Roman governor of Cyprus gave us great joy, and it also laid a solid foundation for the expansion of Christian witness on the island.

And with that behind us we reckoned we were ready to move on. The vast landmass of Asia Minor beckoned.

One day Mark, our mission coordinator, told us that he had booked us a passage on a ship soon to sail from Paphos for Perga in Pamphylia.

Even bigger challenges lay ahead.

Chapter Nine

A LIGHT FOR THE GENTILES

If Paphos had been a scene of a notable spiritual success and an open manifestation of the power of God, our destination, Perga, proved to be the scene of some daunting practical problems. We came crashing back to reality soon after we landed there.

It appeared almost as though Satan, who had suffered a two-nil defeat in the blinding of Bar-Jesus and the conversion of his master, the proconsul, had returned for a rematch with a vengeance. He wasn't going to let us off lightly.

The fight against the forces of evil had only just begun.

Perga in Pamphylia, in the steamy heat of high summer, did not prove a pleasant place to be. Indeed we soon discovered that the city was half-empty, for the more affluent of its citizens had already escaped to their summer retreats up in the cool of the mountains.

The days in that city, which lay on a coastal plain and was surrounded by marshes, were hot and sticky, and in the evenings the clammy, clinging mist was laden with the hoarse croak of frogs, the endless hum of flies and the potentially dangerous bites of myriads of mosquitoes.

And from the mosquitoes came problem number one.

We had scarcely been any more than two weeks in Perga, and were actively considering our next move, when I was struck down with the dreaded, debilitating malaria of the marshes.

My body shook and trembled in spasms, I had a raging fever and a dreadful headache. The pain of this was so severe that it felt as though a tent peg or a flaming arrow had been driven straight through my head. There were times when I thought that my head was going to burst with the agony. And it affected my already weak eyes, too. I could not bear to be in any sort of bright light.

So for days I shivered and shook, burning up with fever, in the semi-dark in a lodging which Mark had procured for us.

When speaking to the locals, Barnabas learnt that the only quick and effective way for me to attain to anything resembling relief from this enervating malady, was to head off up through the Taurus Mountains to a city far above sea level. Antioch in Pisidia was one of a number of places they suggested.

We discussed the matter and considered a move to Antioch to be our best possible plan. Probably only half of the residents in Perga were present in the city, and I was in no fit state to preach there anyway, whereas when we reached the higher, more invigorating altitude of Antioch in Pisidia, I would possibly have regained sufficient strength to make the message known there.

When we had finally decided that I was well enough to travel, perhaps sitting on a donkey for at least part of the way, we suffered our second setback.

It came as a surprise and quite a shock one day when Barnabas informed me that Mark had decided to return to Jerusalem rather than travelling with us up into the mountains.

Not only was I surprised, but I was also deeply disappointed when I heard that news. Mark had been a marvellous help to us in Cyprus, looking after our daily needs, and he had also been growing in confidence every day. He was such a natural in the work and fitted in so well with us. I had harboured high hopes for him. He was a young man who had great potential and I had been convinced that he was set to achieve mighty things for God in later life.

Now he was going back.

Barnabas was embarrassed when I pressed him for a reason for Mark's choice, and I never really received a satisfactory explanation.

Perhaps when he looked up at the Taurus Mountains, some of them still snow-capped even in summer, Mark concluded that to accompany his older cousin and his still ill but incredibly determined companion, up through those high mountain passes where gangs of robbers preyed freely on unsuspecting travellers, was just a trip too far.

Or perhaps he was a bit jealous when he saw that I was now acknowledged as the leader of the party, leaving Barnabas less in the limelight, although the big, gentle, genuine gentleman himself didn't seem to mind in the least.

Or maybe he was simply homesick. Could he be missing his mother and all the buzz of activity in their home, and the familiar sights and sounds of Jerusalem with all the indelible memories of the days when he had seen the Saviour grace its streets? Was this preaching to Roman governors in unfamiliar foreign lands, and talk of penetrating unknown Gentile territory all a bit too much for him, too big a departure from life as he knew it?

Whatever the reason, or reasons, Mark left us a few days before we set off up into the mountains.

He was heading home to a known environment where he would undoubtedly be welcomed.

We were heading away from home to a totally unknown destination, and we had no idea how, or if, we would be welcomed.

But we were going for God.

And we were going in response to a Divine injunction.

We were going 'far hence unto the Gentiles'.

The journey up over the high mountain passes took over a week, stopping in makeshift travellers' shelters on the way. I had to make more stops than some of the others who passed us for I was still very weak from my illness, but as we climbed higher and away from the steaming cauldron of the plains around Perga, I began to feel better. We tried to keep company with other travellers for we reckoned there was safety in numbers, but perhaps we were only making it easy for the robbers. However, the constant contact with others on the road helped keep our spirits up and allowed us, in response to the inevitable question, 'And why are you going to Antioch?' to tell others of the purpose of our trip. Our mission, we informed them with great relish, was to proclaim the good news of the forgiveness of sins through the death, burial and resurrection of the crucified Son of God, Jesus Christ.

As we began to descend on the northern side of the steep mountain passes we were delighted to catch a glimpse of our destination in the distance. Antioch in Pisidia was a Roman colony, and the first impressive structure that we saw as we approached the city reminded us of the influence of the empire upon the civilisation of the world. It was a giant aqueduct, whose arches spanned the plain before the city like a string of colossal camels carved in stone, carrying water to the hundreds of houses straggling across the rocky hillside.

When we eventually entered the city we found it to be a busy, bustling place. Since it was at the crossroads of a number of Roman roads, this Antioch had become an important commercial centre trading in wood, oil, skins, goat's hair and Angora wool.

We were not there to buy and sell, though. We were there to tell the people about Christ.

Our first task in the city was to find somewhere to stay, and when we had that sorted out we set out to find the synagogue. There was a sizeable Jewish settlement in the city and we knew that they must have built a synagogue for the worship of God.

And we were right.

My bout of malaria in Perga had left me drained and after the arduous journey over the mountains I felt utterly washed out, but nothing could keep me from attending the synagogue on the very first Sabbath of our stay in Antioch.

Barnabas and I sat down in that building which had none of the ornate carvings of the heathen temple down the road, but which was still majestic in its simplicity. We had each of us covered our heads with our *tallith*, or veil, which signified that we, although strangers, were qualified to teach in the synagogue.

It was interesting to note the size of the crowd which had assembled for Sabbath worship, and very striking to observe that a fair percentage of them were what we called 'God fearers'. These were mainly people who, disillusioned by the emptiness of their own religion, and attracted by the patent sincerity of the Jews who lived and worked amongst them, had begun to attend the synagogue to hear more about the one true God, creator of heaven and earth.

There was silence for the public readings from the scriptures, one from the Law of Moses, and the other from the prophets. That day they were from the beginning of the book of Deuteronomy, and the beginning of the prophecy of Isaiah.

When the readings were complete and as the scrolls were being returned to their place a clerk came across to where we were sitting with an invitation from the rulers of the synagogue.

"You men who are our brother Jews, if you have any word of encouragement for the people here, say on," he told us.

Although still rather shaky, I saw that this was too good a chance to miss, and just the very opening we had been praying for.

Standing up I made an embracive gesture with my hand, to make sure that all in the building were aware that the 'word of encouragement' I had risen to deliver applied equally to everyone, and then I began by referring to the scriptures which had just been read in our hearing from the law and the prophets.

Having given a brief outline of the history of our nation I then tried to point them to the one to whom all the ancient prophecies pointed, and in whom they were all fulfilled, Jesus Christ.

Then, skipping from past history, I concentrated on pointing out the significance of some comparatively recent events. John the Baptist had been the forerunner who had told of one to come whose shoes he wouldn't even be worthy to unloose. And that Person was the promised One, the Messiah, the Christ.

The rulers at Jerusalem, who should have recognised Him for who He was, didn't, and persuaded Pilate, the Roman governor, to have Him crucified. The story didn't end there either, for Jesus had risen from the dead, and had spoken to many of his friends from Galilee. I then proceeded to prove that even this resurrection of the Messiah had been foretold in the sacred writings.

When satisfied that I had laid a sound base of evidence to prove that Jesus Christ, the crucified carpenter of Nazareth, as I had once described Him, was in fact the true Messiah, I went on to proclaim the purpose of His coming into our world, and our coming to their city.

"You should know, men and brethren," I told them, "That through this man the forgiveness of sins is preached to you, and by him all that believe are justified from all things, from which you could not be justified by the Law of Moses."

The rulers of the synagogue who had been listening intently to me in the earlier historical part of my address, had become rather more restless as I had sought to prove that Jesus Christ was in truth the Anointed of God, and now with this slighting, as they saw it, reference to the Law of Moses they became really agitated.

I saw them scowling across at each other.

Having sat on the same side as men like this in my earlier rabbi days, I could read the signs which were indicating clearly that it was soon time to stop, or an angry argument could ensue. And it was too early in our Antioch expedition for that.

It was time to finish my address with a warning to the sceptical Jewish rulers, and this I did by quoting from the prophets. I decided to hit them hard with Habakkuk.

"Behold, you despisers, and wonder and perish," I quoted, "for I work a work in your days which you shall in no wise believe, though a man declare it unto you."

With that I resumed my seat and the Sabbath worship ended.

The reaction to the proclaimed word was fantastic.

As we tried to push our way out through the crowds who seemed in no hurry to go home, many interested people crowded around us asking questions, and some of the Gentiles, who hadn't been in the synagogue, and other of the proselytes who had, all seemed to want the same thing.

"Come back next week!" they called. "We will all be along to hear you!"

And we didn't even have to wait until the following Sabbath to see the first fruits of that first synagogue sermon, either. Many of the Jews and sincere religious searchers who had been present that day, came to our lodging or met us in the market place and we were able to tell them the story of Jesus. It was most encouraging.

When the next Sabbath day did come around we were amazed at the scene that greeted us when we came near the synagogue. The streets were crowded and the synagogue itself, when we were finally able to push our way into it, was packed. It seemed as though most of the citizens of Antioch had converged on its one small synagogue, the Gentiles outside and the Jews and proselytes inside!

What a hunger to hear the word of God!

This spiritual awakening in Antioch was most gratifying to us, and we took it as a sign of God's stamp of approval on our mission to the city, but the Jewish leaders were not quite so thrilled with it!

They were amazed, alarmed and envious all at once.

How they wondered, could these itinerant preachers, who had suddenly dropped down in amongst them from the snows of the Taurus, accomplish more with one astonishing sermon on the forgiveness of sins through Jesus the Nazarene, than they had done in a lifetime of jealously guarding and systematically teaching the Law and the Prophets?

They found it intolerable, and when I stood up to speak on that second Sabbath they opposed me vigorously. Everything I said they endeavoured to contradict, and when they had run out of logical argument they just combined to shout me down.

It was useless trying to continue.

The message we had come to present was not being heard by the bulk of the people who had come to hear it, so we decided to leave the synagogue.

"We had to come and speak the word of God to you first," we told them above the din, "but because you have rejected it and do not consider yourselves worthy of everlasting life we are now going to turn to the Gentiles."

I could almost feel the excitement of the clamouring crowd from all nationalities, ranks and classes who were thronging around the doorway, straining to hear every word, as I waved my hand towards them and informed the jealous Jewish leaders that I had a command from God, which was summarised in some words by the prophet Isaiah. The storm of dissent subsided somewhat as I began, "I have made you a light for the Gentiles, that you should bring salvation to the ends of the earth."

Then Barnabas and I simply walked out of the synagogue to be encompassed by an even bigger crowd than that of the previous week, eager and anxious to hear more and more of the word of the Lord. They just could not get enough of it.

A time of blessing followed our withdrawal from the synagogue in that city. Many Gentiles believed and were saved, and a church was established.

The Jewish leaders, however, unable to silence us in open confrontation used their influence on many of the wealthy women in the community, some of whom were married to Roman officials, and on some of the leading men themselves, to have us thrown out of the city.

In a very short time an expulsion order had been issued and the pair of us were physically manhandled and deposited outside the city gates. And we were ordered to go on our way immediately.

That was no problem to us by then, though. We simply shook the dust of Antioch out of our sandals as a sign that we were departing, and set off.

A light had been lit and was burning brightly amongst the Gentiles in that city.

We would now carry the torch to somewhere else.

Chapter Ten

A DOOR OF FAITH

As we approached Iconium, after a journey of seventy or eighty miles, my first impression was that it looked from a distance very like Damascus, as I had seen it from the heights before being blinded by the light and love of God on the road outside the city. Iconium was, like its Syrian counterpart, surrounded by high walls, and set in a well-watered plain, and like Damascus it had become important as a centre of culture and commerce, for it was one of the first places where weary travellers could find water, rest and shelter after trekking long distances through apparently endless arid terrain.

When we entered the city and had made a few enquiries, we discovered that Iconium had something else in common with Damascus. Since many of the successful merchants in both cities were Jews, each had within it a thriving Jewish synagogue.

And it was in the synagogue in Iconium that Barnabas and I began to teach, soon after we had found ourselves lodgings in the city.

For months everything went well. Many people listened eagerly as we showed them from their own scriptures that Jesus was the Christ, the Messiah, and that His death on the cross in Jerusalem was not a sign of weakness or failure, but rather of success. He had come to die as an offering to cleanse them from their sin, from which they could never be completely cleansed by the ritual observance of the law.

It had been our experience before, however, and Iconium proved to be no exception to a painfully regular pattern, that when the word of the Lord was being readily received by a sizeable proportion of the people that the Jewish leaders resented it, and us.

After six months or so, the ruling rabbis in the synagogue stirred up both their own people and the local Greek and Roman population, in so far as they could influence them, against us.

We were heretics they said, travelling tricksters, deceiving the people.

That we had learnt how to cope with, for we had heard it so often before.

When some of those who had just recently become believers came to us in some distress, though, to tell us that they were planning to stone us when afforded even half a hint of an opportunity, we decided that it was time to move on.

It would be best for the growing company of Christians if we simply shook the dust of Iconium from our feet, in much the same way as we had done with that of Antioch, and headed off for somewhere else. We were confident that the nucleus of a vibrant new church had been established in the city, and that they were well enough equipped to carry on the work we had begun, at least in the meantime.

So we left them in late spring, promising to pay them a return visit at some stage, and made a short journey south to the nearest settlement of any significance, a town called Lystra.

Although merely twenty miles from Iconium, Lystra was a completely different town altogether. There was no synagogue in that much smaller place for although there were a few isolated Jewish families living in it, there would not have been the ten men required to set one up, according to the Jewish law. On our initial tour of the town we discovered that the sole building dedicated to any kind of worship was an ornate Temple of Zeus that we had passed on the road in.

The townspeople were pagan worshippers of Zeus, who was sometimes called Jupiter, and Mercury, the gods of their mythology. They believed that these deities made periodic appearances in human guise and it was important to avoid mistaking them in their always-unannounced excursions to earth. According to the legends circulating amongst them, some unfortunates had suffered horrendous hardships for failing to identify and satisfy these gods during one of their former unexpected revelations.

We realized at once that we must adopt a different approach in the presentation of the message in Lystra, than we had ever used anywhere else before.

For the benefit of the very few Jews in the town we based our teaching sessions, which were usually in the open air in the marketplace, on the ancient scriptures, but for the benefit of the pagan population we focussed more on the life and death of our Lord, who created all things, but Who had also come to earth as a man in order to provide lasting peace in the lives of those who trusted in Him. Many of the Lystrenians spoke a native dialect, which we had never heard before, but since we soon found out that most of them had a working knowledge of common Greek, we were happy to engage with them in that language.

One of our first meaningful contacts in Lystra, and one which was to prove of lifelong value to me, was made one day in the marketplace. After we had been speaking to a seemingly unappreciative audience, a Jewish woman called Eunice approached us. She had a boy, whom I reckoned to be about fifteen or so, with her, and she introduced him to us as 'my son Timothy'. It appeared that she had been impressed with our teaching and invited us back to her home to meet her ageing mother, Lois, and to hear more about 'this message'.

What a thrill it was to discover that haven of hope in such a heathen city!

What a joy it was to find that these women whom we had just met were Jewesses and that the Holy Scriptures were read regularly in that home!

We soon discovered, in conversation, why this little family group had ended up living in Lystra. Eunice was married to a Greek businessman who worked in the town and thus they had come to settle there.

Barnabas and I counted it a privilege to sit, at the end of many an otherwise unproductive day, with Lois, Eunice, Timothy and the ancient writings with which they were well acquainted, and show them how that Jesus of Nazareth was indeed the Anointed One, promised by the prophets. It gave us great joy to point out from their own scrolls of the scriptures that the so called peasant preacher, who had been utterly and absolutely rejected as a blaspheming nonentity by the Jewish religious establishment, was, despite the paganism prevalent around them, the only true manifestation of God in human form. And how that He had come to earth to procure eternal redemption for mankind.

It was an even bigger, almost unbelievable thrill when all three of them embraced the faith. And it consequently became a singular source of inspiration to us to hear young Timothy repeat the scriptures from memory, as I too had been taught to do as a boy so many years before. He just seemed to blossom forth with every new discussion, for he appeared to have an insatiable desire to uncover more and more of the wonderful meaning of the words which he had been so faithfully taught in his home-school House Of The Book.

Sharing the Gospel in that home was a pleasure and through Eunice and her mother we made some other useful contacts. But reaching the bulk of the population of that spiritually superstitious town was proving a different matter altogether. Although we continued to couch the message in terms that we thought our hearers would understand, we seemed to be making little impact.

So we continued to pray for guidance from God as we awaited what we hoped would be the big breakthrough.

This opportunity came one afternoon when I was speaking to the passers-by in the market place. As I talked to the group of people who had stopped, however briefly, to hear what I had to say, I became aware of a crippled man crouched against a wall. Crippled men crouched against walls were by no means uncommon in the towns and cities we had visited, for the few coins tossed to such people as they begged in public places represented their sole source of income, and hence also their single hope of survival.

This man, who was a well-known character in the town, for he had never walked since he had been a cripple from birth, had an unusual look about him that day, somehow.

As I glanced down at him, while still speaking, I was suddenly struck by an intense sincerity in the returned imploring gaze of the lifelong invalid.

'That man believes that I can heal him through the power of the God I am presenting,' I was immediately convinced.

So, directing my attention totally away from my current address to my largely apathetic audience, I looked straight at him, and as our eyes met, commanded, "Stand up on your feet!"

Suddenly the whole scene changed!

Without hesitation, and with a very natural ease, the crippled man obeyed my order. And not only did the man who had never walked bounce immediately up into a steady standing position, but he also proceeded to pull his few ragged clothes around him and walk away. As he pushed his way through the awestruck bystanders his face was a picture, painted in subtle shades of incredulity and gratitude.

Within seconds a full-blooded outcry had broken forth amongst the people who had been listening no more than half-heartedly to what I had been trying say.

It was a loud, high pitched call in the local vernacular, which neither Barnabas nor I understood. Others took up the exclamation and soon a chanting crowd was fanning out through the narrow streets of the town, proclaiming the message, whatever it was.

Anxious to know what this was all about Barnabas asked one of the few still mute local men.

"They are saying that the gods have come down and visited our town again," the man was happy to interpret. "They are saying that you, because you are taller and of a sort of stately bearing, are Jupiter, the King of gods and men, and that your friend there, who although he is smaller and less striking, seems to do most of the talking for the two of you, is Mercury, the interpreter and prophet of the gods."

Barnabas looked across at me, and I could see he was perplexed.

"What should we do now?" he asked into the air, obviously pondering our best move.

"I think you should go home, or to wherever it is that you are staying, until this frenzy dies down," was the advice of our interpreter who was obviously well attuned to the touchy temperament of his fellow townspeople.

We did as he suggested and soon the initial passion amongst the people seemed to peter out leaving only an eerie emptiness to replace it in the streets.

Late that afternoon, though, we became aware of a renewed clamour and realized that the entire town was buzzing again, and above the increasing hubbub we could hear the lowing of frightened oxen! When we looked out to see what was going on, Barnabas and I discovered that an excited crowd was assembling at the outer gates of the courtyard to our house, and many to them were carrying hefty pieces of wood. The oxen we had heard lowing earlier were standing side by side, bedecked with garlands of fresh flowers.

When we managed to find someone calm enough, and fluent enough in Greek, to explain the significance of all the excitement to us, we were shocked to learn that these Lystrenians were planning to offer the oxen upon a makeshift altar, which they were in the process of building, to us, their gods returned to earth! A white-robed priest of Jupiter seemed to be in charge of operations.

We were horrified.

Running out into the street and in amongst the worked up would-be worshippers, we tried to stop them. Obviously either the bulk of these people had never heard the truth we had come to Lystra to proclaim, or else they hadn't understood it when they heard it.

"Stop! Stop!" we cried. "Don't be building an altar to us! We are just ordinary men like yourselves who have come here to bring you the good news, how that you should turn from these worthless things to the living God!"

The universally accepted sign of the tearing of our clothes, and the sheer intensity of our initial outburst afforded us a lull in their preparation for celebration. And in that lull I went on to further explain our position.

"The God we worship is the one true and living God, the creator of all things," I told them. "In the past our God let all nations go their own way. Yet he didn't leave Himself without a witness on the earth for He has shown us constant kindness by sending rain from heaven and crops in their seasons to provide us with plenty of food for our bodies and joy in our hearts."

Some stopped their activity, confused, if not convinced,

Others carried on regardless, possibly loath to surrender the idea of a banquet of sacrificed bull, but Barnabas and I went in and out amongst them, pleading with them to desist, seeking to point out the folly of the exercise.

After a sustained effort we eventually succeeded in persuading the people to forget the notion of doing homage, or offering sacrifices to us, and to go home.

This they did in sullen silence.

The discarded garlands, trampled flat or blown and strewn around in pathetic pointless petals, seemed to summarize the mood of the moment.

Nobody was very happy. In fact the reprieved oxen were the only creatures with cause to thank us for our intervention that afternoon

Our success in thwarting their purposes had angered the temple priests.

Our exposure of the folly of their religion had embittered most of the local populace.

For days after that incident we felt a curious coldness as we tried to continue our regular witness in the marketplace. Although some people had embraced the message and become believers, including one very thankful healed cripple, the vast majority of the residents of Lystra either ignored us completely, or shouted insults as they passed.

A bonfire of resentment was building up in the town.

It would take only one small spark to start a major conflagration, we knew.

That spark was provided a few weeks later when a group of Jewish merchants came down from Antioch and Iconium to Lystra to buy grain in the autumn markets.

As soon as they discovered that we were living and teaching in the town they stirred up trouble for us. They provided the single spark needed to ignite the building up bonfire of resentment into a raging inferno of revenge.

When they had heard the story of the healing of the cripple and the obstructed offering, from some of the still rather bewildered townspeople and traders of Lystra, they seized what was for them an ideal opportunity to do us down.

"Don't listen to those men," they advised. "We had them banned from Antioch and they just escaped from Iconium before we had them stoned!"

"But the small one, the one that does the most of the talking, performed a mighty miracle here. There can be no doubt about that," the men of the town responded, becoming increasingly confused. "So if they are not gods, as we thought at first, who or what *are* they?"

"They are wicked magicians," whispered the men from Antioch and Iconium. "They are nothing but tricksters. Deceivers. Conmen. Don't listen to them. Chase them. You would be doing your gods a good turn if you stoned them out of here!"

For some strange reason this seemed to sound like sense to the deflated men of Lystra. They, and indeed also their long-held traditional beliefs, had been made to both look and sound stupid by the intervention of these vagrants.

And so they determined to get their own back.

Some of our Christian friends in the town had heard of the villainous advice of these bitter Jews, and alerted us to the possibility of things to come.

Since we had no way of knowing, however, if, or when, or in what form, retribution would be exacted, we continued to teach in the streets as usual.

Then it happened.

Late one afternoon when I was speaking to a small group of mildly interested men, a mob of twenty or thirty assailants with stones in their hands and evil in their eyes, descended upon me.

A few of them I recognised as Jews from their dress and general appearance, but the most of them were disaffected locals.

"Stone him! Get him! Away with him!" they yelled as they approached.

I was surrounded in seconds.

The people who had once wanted to worship me now wanted to kill me. It all sounded so familiar. Peter had told me how that the very same thing had happened to Jesus in Jerusalem.

Huge stones began to rain down on my body. I could feel them tearing at my clothing, then punching and piercing my skin. The unexpected ferocity of the onslaught forced me to my knees.

For a fleeting moment I thought about Stephen that day outside the Holy City. Now the wheel had come full circle. I was being served up another dose of my own medicine. This must have been how he had felt.

"Lord, don't blame them for this," had been his final prayer.

Could I bring myself to adopt that gracious attitude?

I was struggling valiantly to think forgiving thoughts when there was a massive thump on the back of my head.

Everything went black...

When I began to regain consciousness I was aware of voices. They seemed far away in the distance at first, but as I gradually came round I realized that there were people around me.

Anxious voices drifted into my reawakening hearing.

"We can't just leave him here overnight or the jackals will get him," someone was saying.

"We can carry him back into the city at dusk," came the answer to that problem.

Then came a strong voice I recognised so well.

"How am I ever going to break this news to the brethren back in Antioch?" was the problem it wanted to address.

It was Barnabas.

Everyone was suddenly struck dumb when I started to stir.

And when I stood up that loyal little band rushed to embrace me, one by one!

"Oh Paul, we thought we had lost you!" some of them exclaimed with joy.

I was particularly touched by the look of inexpressible ecstasy on the tear-stained face of young Timothy. He, maybe more than most, would have been disappointed to lose me, for we had spent many profitable hours together as he had quizzed both Barnabas and me about the scriptures and the life and work of the emergent church in Jerusalem and Antioch.

When I found that I could walk, albeit rather stiffly, my friends escorted me to the home where we had often resorted in days of discouragement, that of Eunice, Lois, and of course, Timothy.

As my dear friends tended my battered body, bathing the congealed blood of some of the more serious wounds, Barnabas and I took the obvious decision. We would have to leave Lystra as soon as possible. It could be dangerous, not only for us, but also to this band of faithful Christians, if we were to stay any longer.

So in the morning, despite my injuries, and with each of us equipped only with his cloak, his staff, and the packed lunch of bread and dried olives that Eunice had so hastily put together, we set off from Lystra, in the direction of Derbe.

On arriving, after a slower than usual journey, at this destination we were pleased to find ourselves far enough away from agitating Jewish influences to be permitted to preach the gospel in peace. And that is what we did, all through the winter, when travel would have been impossible anyway with the mountain passes blocked by snow.

God blessed our ministry in Derbe and many of the citizens of that strategic city trusted in Christ and a thriving church community was established.

With the coming of the increasing warmth of spring the next year we decided that it was time to move on again and concluded that before seeking to evangelise anywhere else, we should report back to the believers in our home church in Antioch in Syria.

This presented us with a practical problem.

Which way should we go? For we did have a choice.

We could take the shorter route down through the Taurus Mountains to the Cilician Gates, through my home city of Tarsus, and hence on to Antioch. Or, alternatively, we could go back the way we had come, retracing our steps through Lystra, Iconium and the other Antioch.

And our second option was the one we decided to take up.

As we reflected upon it, Barnabas and I recognised that we had been forcibly expelled from all three of these cities leaving the new believers largely uninstructed. It would be imperative to afford much needed encouragement to, and establish an orderly structure of leadership amongst, each of the groups.

Although this took much more of our time that the shorter route by Tarsus would have done, it proved eminently worthwhile. The Christians were almost overwhelmed to see us again.

It was wonderful!

And the reception they gave us was almost matched by the unbelievable welcome we received when we arrived back in our home base in Antioch.

It took us more than two weeks to tell them of all that had happened in the more than two years we had been away.

I told them humbly how that I now believed that God had begun to fulfil His purpose for me, in me.

A door of faith had been opened wide to the Gentiles. And many of them, from different cultures and different classes in different cities had gladly entered it.

It was a door, too, that I could have been killed pushing open, but for the preserving grace of God.

Chapter Eleven

STOP YOUR PLAY-ACTING PETER

It was such a thrill to be back in Antioch. All the Christians there were so happy to hear of the many people who had come to know Christ as Saviour through our ministry.

The buzz of excitement that accompanied our return to Antioch had reached Jerusalem, and had begun to reverberate all around the church there, too, within a month or so. Some, but sadly, not all, of the believers there had been pleased to hear of the work of God in Galatia, and the first of these to make a point of visiting us and hearing more about our expedition was Peter. Since the hub of Christian activity had long since moved north from Jerusalem to Antioch he seemed to have no qualms about travelling north to hear of our personal accounts of our many experiences.

And we shared countless precious times together.

It took me back in happy thought to the times when Peter and I had so often talked on late into the night the first time I had met him in Jerusalem. Barnabas had played an important part in bringing us together on that occasion and he was still present and important at the latest reunion.

There was a vast difference, however, between those early Jerusalem meetings, and the Antioch fellowship nights.

In Jerusalem we had been Jews of 'the Way' talking to other Jews of 'the Way'.

In Antioch, Titus the Greek, Lucius and Simeon from North Africa, and a number of other Gentile believers were there too.

In Antioch, we were Christians, reporting to other Christians from a wide range of cultural and religious backgrounds, how that other Gentiles from an equally wide range of cultural and religious backgrounds had turned to become Christians.

Peter really revelled in it.

The lesson he had learnt from God through the conversion of Cornelius the centurion seemed to have broadened his mind. He had no reservations whatsoever in joining us in our many communal meals as we shared these precious matters together.

All went well, for a while.

All was wonderful, for a while.

But it wasn't set to last.

The sense of peace and purpose that had pervaded the church for so long was shattered, crushed to pieces, all in the course of a matter of days, one week, with the arrival of a group of believers from the Jerusalem church.

These men said that they had been sent from James, with a message for Peter, but it didn't take me long to discover that they were operating their own agenda. I could sense trouble from the moment they arrived amongst us, for below a veneer of friendship I could detect an only-thinly veiled opposition.

As soon as these men had fixed themselves up with somewhere to stay in the city they began to subvert our stability by introducing subtle questions about the importance of the, as they saw it, sidelined, Law of Moses, in the minds of all the believers in Antioch who had hailed from a Jewish background.

Then, a few weeks later, when they had prepared the soil with the plough of doubt, they were ready for a more widespread broadcasting of their contaminated seed. This they began to sow quite openly in our meetings by standing up and boldly asserting that unless believers were circumcised, as commanded by the Law of Moses, they could not be saved. What they were saying in effect was that Gentiles had to become Jews before they could become Christians!

This teaching precipitated terrible, and to me terrifying, trouble amongst us!

It upset all the believers from the Jewish tradition because they began to wonder whether they should be associating so freely with 'uncircumcised' Gentiles, whether Christian or not.

And it caused complete consternation amongst the Gentile Christians. If they had to obey some requirement of the Mosaic Law, which they knew nothing whatsoever about, in order to be saved, then they weren't saved at all!

Worse, though, was yet to come, for Peter, who throughout his lifetime had been consistently inconsistent, changed his attitude and approach completely. As soon as those blustering Judaists began insisting on circumcision as a condition of salvation, he started withdrawing himself from the homes of many of the Gentile believers with whom he had up until then shared such intimate fellowship. It would be wrong, under the ancient law, to even eat with such people, he knew. He had obviously chosen to conveniently forget the vision of the unclean beasts in the letdown sheet.

Peter's vacillation really surprised, and sickened me, but I was aware of his forever impulsive and unpredictable nature. When Barnabas, however, who had been my loyal companion in travel and who had been so vocal in his earlier opposition to these troublemakers from Judea, began to make feeble excuses for not sharing meetings with some of the respected Gentile elders, and for not visiting them in their homes, I heard alarm bells ringing loud and clear.

Something would have to be done, and soon, if the church wasn't to be split right down the middle.

I felt rather isolated and alone as I tried to decide upon the most appropriate course of action, so I spent much time before God in prayer.

To me this was more than just a fall-out about a foible of the Jewish law. There were far wider implications.

If, for instance, this teaching was correct, then the way of salvation through simple faith in Christ alone was under siege, and my calling and commission to go forth with the gospel to the Gentiles, would require immediate and radical review.

And in addition to that, Barnabas and I had been wasting our time in Cyprus and Galatia, for most of those who had come to own Christ as Saviour on that often hazardous mission, were still-uncircumcised Gentiles!

The most direct approach, I reckoned, would be the most effective in this situation, so I decided to adopt the old well established rule of confrontation, to 'pick out the ringleader and hit him hard'.

I challenged Peter in a public meeting.

It was a big thing for me to confront such a figurehead, but it had to be done.

"Stop your play-acting, Peter," I implored him in one of our gatherings, with everyone present. "How is that you, who, though a Jew, have been living happily amongst the Gentiles, are now trying, all of a sudden, to force Gentile believers to conform to Jewish laws? You know as well as I know, that whoever we are, whether Jew or Gentile, we are justified not by the keeping of the law, but by faith in Christ. Nobody can be saved by observing the law, so why make it a condition of salvation?"

Thankfully Peter saw sense, admitted his mistake, and apologised to his Gentile brethren. Barnabas, too, seemed to regret his uncharacteristic, but short-lived lapse, and the sharing, caring attitude, which had been so long the hallmark of our church, returned.

Those who couldn't seem to free themselves from an unbending insistence upon imposing the ancient laws of their nation upon all believers, weren't happy, however.

They had been defeated in Antioch, but requested that the matter be debated in full, in the presence of the apostles and elders, in that centre where the law of Moses had for so long been the standard for all religious belief, but where also the death of Christ on the cross out at Calvary had ushered in the era of salvation by faith in Him, Jerusalem.

Perhaps they thought that Peter would buckle again in the presence of James, who was reputed to be a stickler for the law, but I didn't mind. I was convinced that he wouldn't, and I was every bit as well versed in the law as any of the would-be opposition, for I had been educated in the rabbinical schools just as them.

I would be happy to set forth the truth of God, as it had been revealed to me, before anybody! And anyway, it would be important to have this matter cleared up, once and for all, and to the satisfaction of all.

In various groups, and at various times, we made our way south to Jerusalem.

The dissenting and disruptive, and by then also deeply disgruntled, delegation, left first, followed by a suitably subdued and hence hopefully more predictable Peter.

Barnabas and I followed a few weeks later when we had satisfied ourselves that it was safe to leave without any fear of a repeat of the ill-feeling that had been caused in the church by the unfortunate intervention of the meddling men from Jerusalem.

The previous two groups of travellers may have hurried south to the ancient capital, but we took it slowly, stopping off with a number of church groups on the way through Phoenicia and Samaria to report on the conversion of the Gentiles on our recent trip. We didn't stop at all in Judea, though, for many of the churches there had a strong Jewish bias, and we wanted to leave all the discussion until the discussion, which we hoped would end all discussions, in Jerusalem!

When we eventually arrived in the Holy City we discovered that our visit had been long awaited and much anticipated and were very warmly welcomed.

Those of the party of the Pharisees, who had been so active in opposition in Antioch, had been diligently preparing their case for weeks. So when the evening of the meeting finally came around they could barely wait for the formal introductions to be completed before one of the chief agitators jumped up, exclaiming, "We must compel these Gentiles to be circumcised and obey the Law of Moses!"

"The church is going to be swamped by these foreigners if we don't!" someone else contended.

"Are we being asked to abandon the Law and the Prophets, which our fathers have for so long held so dear, forever?" another wanted to know.

A lively debate ensued.

Everyone was given a chance to have his say. All views were aired.

However, when Peter took increasingly raised voices to be an indicator of increasingly raised tempers, he stood up to make his considered contribution.

His final judgement on the matter would be welcomed and respected by all, so the listeners slipped into an uneasy silence, when he stood up and raised his hand.

After our experience in Antioch I wondered what he would say. And as I glanced around the audience I could see that several of the Pharisees in the church were also obviously anxious about his response.

Peter had such a wealth of experience behind him, and such a profound love for his Lord within him, that everybody looked up to him, but nobody was ever sure what to expect from him. No one could ever be totally and entirely sure how he was going to react in any given situation. Or what he was going to come out with next!

His summing-up on that occasion was a masterstroke, however.

My direct confrontation appeared to have had the desired effect.

There was certainly no play-acting this time.

Peter just told them what he really believed.

In his speech he began by taking a step back into recent history, reminding the audience that God had called him, ten years before, to lead a Gentile centurion to Christ. There had been a bit of a fuss about that at the time, but with the passing of the years it had become accepted. He then proceeded to contend that since God had given the Holy Spirit to both Jews and Gentiles on equal terms, why should the Jews seek to impose the terms of their law, from which they themselves had been freed through faith in Christ, upon their Gentile fellow-believers?

It was somewhat ironic, and it made me smile quietly to myself, when I heard him use the same argument to the concerned company in Jerusalem, as I had used to him before an equally concerned company in Antioch, some months before. His parting shot, his summing-up of the summing-up, was the thought of salvation by grace for all, Jew and Gentile alike.

"We believe that it is through the grace of our Lord Jesus Christ that we are saved, just as they are," he announced emphatically, and sat down.

The earlier restlessness had gone from the audience by then. Peter had stilled them into a complete and utter submissive silence, and when Barnabas and I were invited to tell of the working of God amongst the Gentile nations we were afforded rapt and uninterrupted attention.

Gasps of disbelief punctuated by nods of approval greeted such stories as the blinding of Bar-Jesus and the salvation of Sergius Paulus, the Roman proconsul on Cyprus, and the healing of the lame man, followed by the spurned sacrifices and subsequent stoning, at Lystra.

When we had finished our detailed account of our experiences James stood up to bring the matter to an ultimate conclusion, by summarizing the general consensus of the meeting.

I knew that whatever he said would be accepted. James was known as 'The Just', because of his reputation for godly righteousness. His decision, like that of Peter, would carry much weight.

He began his verdict by referring to what Peter had said, and then, I thought very diplomatically, to the prophets of the Holy Scriptures, pointing out that Amos had predicted that God would 'take from the Gentiles a people for Himself'.

"It is my judgement that we shouldn't create problems for the Gentiles who are turning to God," he went on, "but there are a few matters about which I think we should write to them."

The few matters, which he wanted to write to them about, were interesting, and showed a God-given depth of understanding. They would certainly promote peace and reconciliation between the two different traditions within the growing church.

He advocated that the Gentile Christians be asked to refrain from idolatry and immorality, both of which were prevalent in their society and civilisation, but both of which were prohibited by Jewish law. Then, bearing in mind the fact that many of the church meetings were held in homes, and often included communal meals, he proposed that the Gentile believers be ask to respect the scruples of their Jewish counterparts and not eat any food which they would consider 'unclean', in their presence.

It was a very mature judgement, liberating the Gentile believers from any obligation to keep the Law of Moses, but yet expecting mutual tolerance and consideration from every Christian, whatever his or her background.

Everyone seemed to concur completely with that outcome and two prominent men called Judas and Silas were appointed to accompany us back to Antioch to covey the decision to the church there, and farther afield as occasion arose.

When the elders had drafted a letter to the Christians at Antioch, offering their apology for the distress caused amongst them by the self-appointed deputation from Jerusalem, explaining the role of Judas and Silas, and expressing their ultimate judgement on the position of Gentiles in the church, we set off with it. I must say I found it rather gratifying that Barnabas and I were referred to in that letter as, 'our beloved brethren Barnabas and Paul, men who have hazarded their lives for the Lord Jesus'.

Now we were all one in Christ Jesus, striving towards the same ultimate goal of seeing men and women, whoever they were, or wherever they came from, coming to know Jesus Christ as Lord of their lives through faith in Him alone.

We made very few stops on our way back north with that letter in our possession. There was little time to spend with the churches with whom we had stopped on the way south, but the journey did give us the opportunity to get to know Judas and Silas better. I was fascinated to discover, in the course of conversation, that Silas was, like myself, a Roman citizen.

Our return to Antioch was once more greeted with great rejoicing, and when the letter we had brought from Jerusalem was read at the next packed-out meeting of the church everyone was mightily relieved.

Our brethren could now live in peace, both with one another and with the Lord.

Another obstacle had been overcome, for an issue which had threatened to split the church in two, right down the middle, had been resolved and removed, we hoped forever.

Now Barnabas and I could get on with the main business of our lives, which was instructing and exhorting the many who were coming to Christ, and beaming out the illuminating rays of the light of faith to the Gentile nations.

Chapter Twelve

PICKING THE TEAM TO TRAVEL

After a few months of the most agreeable fellowship in Antioch, I began to realize that the time had come to move on again. I couldn't stay there for the rest of my life. My mind had begun to revert repeatedly to the churches that Barnabas and I had been so privileged to see established on our first trip.

There were so many both mature and gifted leaders in the church in the place where we were, and yet I was convinced that some of the more recently formed fellowships, in places where we had once been, but now were not, would really appreciate some support and encouragement. And on a personal level, too, I longed to meet all of those dear Christians again. Some of them had suffered a lot for the sake of the Gospel, and I was sure that it would give them a genuine boost to see a friendly face or two once more.

When spring came around, the variety of goods on sale in the shops on the magnificent Street of the Colonnades increased. Since this was a sure sign that the ships had begun to ply more frequently to the port of Seleucia, I put a proposal to Barnabas one evening.

It had just dropped down dark, and as we were walking and talking our way home from a church gathering where a capacity crowd had enjoyed the peaceful presence of God for almost two hours, I said, "There are plenty of responsible brethren here in Antioch to carry on the work now, so I was wondering how you would feel about the pair of us making a return visit to all those cities where we preached the word of the Lord last time, and see how they are getting along? I'm sure they could do with a bit of help and support."

"Yes, I had been wondering about that myself," my friend replied. He walked on a few more steps, with his head bowed as though contemplating something either very deep or very difficult, before adding, "And we could take John Mark with us again. I think he realizes that he made a big mistake and let himself, and us, down badly, when he heard our reports of what had happened after he left us on the last trip."

"No, really, I don't think that would be very wise, Barnabas," was my instant reaction to that suggestion. "If John Mark deserted us before, would he not be very likely to do it again? We couldn't possibly set out to face the hardships that you know we would have to face, with somebody who is liable to let us down halfway through when the going gets rough."

"I know, and as I have just said, I think *he* knows, that he let us down once," Barnabas was forced to admit. "But because he failed once, does that mean he is to be branded a failure for the rest of his life? Is there no such thing as a second chance with you, Paul? Remember what Peter told us one night about the day he asked The Master about how many times he should forgive a brother who sinned against him? Peter says he suggested up to seven times but Jesus advocated up to seventy times seven. Where is your sense of forgiveness?"

"This isn't just a matter of forgiveness, Barnabas," I retorted impatiently, struggling to control my mounting indignation. "This is more a matter of simple, practical common sense. John Mark is a sincere young man, right enough, and a kinsman of your own, but say we take him with us, and halfway through some difficult set of circumstances somewhere he decides to go back home to Jerusalem to his mother, where would we be then? And when you are into quoting The Master, I seem to recall that he also said that 'he who puts his hand to the plough and looks back is not fit for the kingdom of God'. To me Mark has put his hand to the plough and has not only looked back, but has *gone* back, so he is not fit to go again!"

"Do I take it then that you have definitely decided that you will not be taking him with you again?" Barnabas could constrain his frustration, at what he saw as my unforgiving intransigence, no longer.

"That's exactly right! I have definitely decided that I will not be taking him with me again. He is too big a liability!" I roared back.

Things were turning unbelievably ugly.

It was almost unthinkable! Two bosom friends, who had been through so much together for the love of God and the sake of the Gospel, were reduced to standing yelling at each other in the street!

We were absolutely mad at each other!

We had overcome far bigger problems than this one in our wonderful years of work and witness together. But neither of us was willing to back down now.

"All right, then! If that's the way you want it, we will split up!" Barnabas stormed, after we had glared daggers at each other for a minute or two. " I will take John Mark and go somewhere, and you can take whoever you like, and go wherever you like!"

That evening ushered in yet another sleepless night for me. My restless mind robbed my restless body of any rest it was due.

How stupid! I thought on reflection. Barnabas and I had both wanted to do what was best in the service of God, but best in what aspect of the service of God, had been our bone of contention.

He saw the possibility of what God could do for the individual, John Mark, and I saw the possibility of what John Mark could not do for God. He was, understandably, concerned with the personal development of a faltering fellow-Christian, and I was, equally understandably, I tried to console myself, concerned with the successful advancement of the Gospel of Christ.

The rift was unfortunate, and proved irreconcilable.

Within a month, Barnabas had set off with John Mark to Cyprus, which was his home island and also where Mark had already been, leaving me to choose 'whoever I liked' to go with to 'wherever I liked'. And obviously now, also, 'whenever' I liked!

Since Barnabas had gone to the first of the locations we had visited on our trip together, Cyprus, I had more than one reason for deciding to go to the other, south Galatia.

Choosing a travelling companion, out of all those who would have been willing to accompany me, was not difficult. One man had headed my short list of prospective new team members in the work of the Lord, for some months, indeed from the time we had journeyed back from Jerusalem together.

His name was Silas.

To me, this man appeared to have everything. He was a levelheaded, sensible believer, with an unswerving loyalty to the Lord, and a sincere commitment to His work. He had been a member of the 'mother' church in Jerusalem when I had first come across him, and yet he seemed equally at home in, and was undoubtedly respected by, the more cosmopolitan congregation in Antioch.

Silas had been one of those appointed to carry the circular letter in relation to the Gentile attitude to the Jewish laws, and if need be explain the finer points of the decision on those matters to any church company with questions. This could prove to be an invaluable asset when it came to presenting the letter to the church groups I planned to visit, throughout Cilicia, and later on, Galatia.

And to me the ultimately decisive factor in choosing Silas as my companion, the bonus to beat all bonuses, was his Roman citizenship. That in itself could prove priceless should we ever decide to push westward towards the edge of Europe.

I had no regrets, either, about that choice, for after the church in Antioch had commended us, we set out, not by sea as Barnabas and Mark had done, but overland towards the north-west, through the remainder of Syria and into Cilicia.

We passed through many towns and cities in my home province, including Tarsus, the city where I was born. It was good to introduce Silas to the members of the small group of believers in that city, and to share the message of the circular letter with them, but I had no intention of stopping over in Tarsus. I wanted to keep pushing onward, for I had other important places to visit, and other important people to see.

As Silas and I trudged up through the narrow pass in the Taurus Mountains, known as the Cicilian Gates, we had to stop and stand to the side often to allow the camel trains of the traders to make their way down towards the markets in the cities on the plains below. And it was during those slowly climbing days, too, that I shared my vision for the days to come with my new companion, whom I had already come to trust completely.

My aim, I told him, was to press as far westward and northward as I could, proclaiming the message of the gospel to the Gentile nations who had never heard the name of Jesus, and to instruct and encourage all the Christians we met on the way through.

Since Silas had been well acquainted, too, with the reasons behind my sad separation from Barnabas, I mooted to him a plan that I had, which I firmly believed had been given me by God. This was to enlist a young brother called Timothy, from Lystra, to join us as we pushed westward. Silas could judge the suitability of the young man for such a mission, himself, when we reached the town where he lived with his godly mother and grandmother, I told him.

When we had travelled for a further two days in the welcome warmth of the sunshine after emerging from the deep and dark upward rising ravines of the Cicilian Gates, the first city we came to however, was not Lystra, but Derbe.

And as soon as I met the Christians there I was confronted with an unforeseen, and momentarily upsetting, blast from the past.

Completely ignoring my new companion they rushed up to me, individually and in groups exclaiming, "Oh Paul, it's marvellous to see you again, but where's Barnabas? Whatever happened to him? Is he ill, or what?"

Anxious to tell the truth, without inflicting any pain on anyone, I explained to them that Barnabas and I had decided to lead separate expeditions, he to Cyprus, and me to Galatia. I then introduced Silas to them, and when he had read aloud, and outlined the reasons for, and meaning behind the letter from Jerusalem, everyone was quite content and we enjoyed some happy times there for a number of weeks.

It was soon time to move on, and I was glad, not that I had any overwhelming urge to leave the saints at Derbe, but I did have a great desire to be with the saints at Lystra, and some of them in particular.

As we approached the city where I had been stoned I was able to point out two notable sites of historical interest to Silas. One was the spot by the roadside where I had been dumped and left for dead, and the other was the elaborate Temple of Zeus where I could have been worshipped as a god, had I so desired.

"Living for God, has never been dull for you, Paul!" Silas remarked with a smile as we entered though the gates and on into the town.

The believers, and especially Lois, Eunice and Timothy, were delighted to see us once more, but all of their opening questions were along exactly the same lines as those I had been bombarded with in Derbe.

"Where's Barnabas?" they were anxious to know. "Is he well enough? Is he still as active as ever in the work of the Lord?"

"He is a lovely man, a really good man," I heard someone else remark.

I had to agree with him, in truth, for I knew that I owed my reception into the early church in Jerusalem to the intervention of the big genial Jewish Cypriot, and my introduction to the abundant work of the Lord in Antioch to his selfless sagacity.

That was altogether too painful for me to contemplate, however, and so I quickly gave the stock explanation of the 'dividing up of the work', and tried to relegate Barnabas to the back of both my mind, and theirs.

As time passed in that town, no one knew but Silas that I had been discreetly observing the quiet and gentle demeanour of young Timothy, whom I guessed to be about eighteen years of age, and listening to him and drawing him out as we discussed the scriptures and the ways and work of God together.

Within a few weeks I was more convinced than ever that I should invite him to join us in the ministry of the Gospel. Silas agreed with me, commenting on the warm and wonderful esteem in which he was held, not only amongst the Christians there in Lystra, but amongst others who had come over to visit us from the neighbouring city of Iconium also.

One evening as we were all sitting together, having just enjoyed some of Eunice's hospitality, I broached the subject.

" I was wondering if Timothy here would like to join Silas and me in the work of the Lord?" I enquired. "Someone younger could be a great practical help to us in a number of ways, and he would also be gaining valuable experience. We are not going to be able to stick this pace forever and we need younger brethren coming on to take over the reins."

Lois and Eunice looked at each other, their expressions a quaint mixture of pride, puzzlement, pain and pleasure.

Timothy just grew red with embarrassment and looked long and hard at the floor.

To give them a chance to further consider my proposal I went on to explain. "We need someone to do for us what John Mark did for Barnabas and me on Cyprus, and for months now, I have believed before God that Timothy is the person best suited to fulfil that role. He is possessed with an exceptional gracious maturity combined with a profound spiritual insight for someone of his age. Will you all consider that idea together and let us know soon what you think?"

Having discussed the matter further we left Timothy to consider the proposition with his mother and grandmother, and in the presence of God.

And I continued to pray for guidance, as I had done so often before.

Within a week we were back in the house and were pleased to learn that Timothy had decided to join us on our travels when we left Lystra.

It soon became obvious that this decision was set to take more out of the two saintly ladies, than it was out of Timothy. For him this could be the beginning of a life spent in the service of the Lord whom he loved. What an unspeakable privilege that would be!

For his mother and grandmother, however, it represented the removal from their immediate patch of sky, the sole star of their lives.

When it came time to make final preparations for leaving I told Silas one day that I thought it would be best if Timothy would consent to undergo the Jewish ritual of circumcision.

Silas was completely taken aback by the idea, and said so.

"What do you mean, Paul?" he asked, obviously flummoxed. "After all the fuss about circumcision in Jerusalem, and after freeing the Gentiles from the yoke of the law, and that not without an often bitter struggle, now you are proposing to circumcise Timothy! And I am carrying a letter about in my pouch telling the churches that circumcision isn't necessary, yet you are going to impose it on this fine young man! Am I hearing right?!"

His concern, and indeed his confusion, were understandable.

"You are right, Silas," I told him in reply. "You know, and I know, that circumcision is nothing, and uncircumcision is nothing, but faith in Christ is everything. What we are talking about here now though, is not a question of doctrine but of diplomacy. Although Timothy's father was Greek, his mother is a Jewess, and because of that he will be recognised as a Jew everywhere he goes. As an uncircumcised Jew he will never be admitted to any synagogue we propose to visit. And that could present us with endless problems."

When he had given my argument some serious consideration Silas saw the logic of my line of thought and Timothy was duly further prepared practically to follow His Lord effectively, wherever He would choose to lead.

Lois and Eunice tried bravely to bear up on the morning of parting. It must have been so difficult for them.

On one hand they were thrilled to see their talented treasure set out to labour for the Lord, yet their hearts were breaking in two to see him go.

As we strode out the city gate and on towards Iconium, I knew that God had guided me to His man. Timothy would become, I was convinced, a champion for the faith.

In the meantime, however, he seemed happy just to stride out for his God, in the company of two of God's more mature servants, and one of them being, I was to discover later, his boyhood hero.

For those first few months, though, I would not have blamed our newly recruited assistant if he had occasionally doubted the wisdom of leaving home to work with us.

It seemed that nothing was working out right. Nothing seemed to go as we had planned it. We tried to go places, and God closed the doors. It was a trying time.

Then to make matters worse I fell sick again. The malaria came back with a vengeance, as I was to find to my cost, it was liable to do when I became overly tired, which was nearly always.

For I had a habit of driving myself to the limit of my physical endurance. Nearly always. And never for myself, but always for God and His glorious Gospel.

This particular bout of illness, though devastating at the time, was to prove a blessing from God in the long run for it was while recuperating from it that I felt impelled to press on westward towards Troas on the seacoast.

I couldn't explain this mysterious urge to get to Troas at the time, other than that God was somehow behind it, and therefore I was quite happy to do it.

We weren't long there, however, until a young Greek doctor, arrived at the house where we had found a lodging. He said that he had heard of me from some clients of his who had come all the way over from Antioch in Pisidia, and he knew two things about me. Some of the people he had been talking to were Christians who had told him of the message that Barnabas and I had been preaching some years before, so he knew that I was a sent servant of my Heavenly Father. And he had also heard from some of the locals in Troas that I had been sick, so he came to offer his services as a physician.

There are some people that you like as soon as you meet them, and this well read, and softly spoken doctor, who told us to call him Luke, was one of those people for me.

When he volunteered to call with me every day to monitor my physical condition, I prayed earnestly that I would be given the opportunities, and the appropriate words, to address his spiritual condition. For days he came to see me, and for days I talked to him about Christ. He was a clever man with a wide knowledge of the religious systems of the day, but no personal faith.

However, after a number of mutual consultations, I had the thrill of leading Luke to my Lord. Then, when he heard of our desire to spread the word of God throughout the world, he offered to join us. He was so thrilled with his newly found faith that he wanted to stay close to Silas and myself to learn as much as he possibly could about the abundant mysteries of the Christian gospel, in as short a time as possible. Luke had, I could soon see, an ever inquisitive mind, much like my own, and a mind like that, if dedicated to God, could bring tremendous blessing to the work of God, and the children of God, in days to come.

Luke would come, like Silas, with a built in bonus, too. He could, he said, look after the medical needs of all of us, and practice medicine if necessary to help pay our bills.

So now we were four.

Things had come a long way from the night Barnabas and I had parted so acrimoniously in Antioch.

God had, in His amazing providence, provided me with a multinational team.

We were two Jews with Roman citizenship, one Jew who was also half-Greek, and a full-blooded Greek. Together we represented the three major cultural systems of the known world so we were ideally equipped to witness in any society, anywhere.

And we were, each and every one of us, willing to lay down his life for his Lord.

All we needed to know from Him now was, Where?

Chapter Thirteen

HELP!

Troas was a busy seaport where east met west, where the traders arriving by sea from ports in Europe met up with traders arriving overland from the hinterland of Asia.

I enjoyed a few days of recuperation there, just wandering around the city, familiarizing myself with its crowded thoroughfares and soaking up all the sights and sounds of such a bustling centre of commerce.

Our new friend, and enthusiastic convert to the Christian faith, Luke, seemed particularly interested in the sea and ships, so he and I spent many hours down by the harbour together. Those were both pleasant and profitable times as we discussed everything from the marvellous mysteries of the faith to the price of figs, while watching the numerous vessels coming and going, depositing or dispatching a wide variety of both passengers and produce either on or from the quayside.

When walking through the streets of the city, whether alone or with some of the others of the group, I used to amuse myself by trying to guess the nationality of some of the hordes of passing people from their natural, and often distinctive physical features, and their different, and often gaudy by conservative Jewish standards, national dress.

It was an infinitely bigger challenge to me, however, as a specially commissioned beacon to beam the light of the glorious Gospel of God to the Gentile nations, to see so many diverse nations represented in one city.

How would I begin to tell them, or even some of them, about Christ, whom I loved and served?

Where should I begin?

One evening at dusk I stood with Silas and Timothy gazing out across the reddening expanse of the Aegean Sea. It was so still. The seawater slapping and sucking at the softly swishing small smooth stones along the shoreline made the only sound to slice open the silence.

Beyond the island of Samothrace, which had already become silhouetted in the sunset, lay the distant, and only faintly visible, hills of Macedonia, the northern province of Greece.

It seemed so very far away, and yet, in a strange sense, so very near.

It was a different country, in a different continent, but it was still comparatively close.

It was also, however, only one of any number of places which would be easily accessible from the crossroads city of Troas.

A few nights later, as I slept, God showed me His will for my work, in a vision.

As I lay in bed, sound asleep, I saw, as though standing right beside me, a man from Macedonia. And he was calling me.

There could be no mistaking the identity of the man. Nobody could miss a Macedonian. It was Luke who had first pointed them out to me down by the harbour, and up through the streets. The travellers and traders from that province wore a particular style of Greek mantle and a broad brimmed sunhat to protect them from the searing sun.

You could spot a Macedonian a mile away!

And there could be no mistaking the clarity or the urgency of his message, either.

"Come over into Macedonia and help us!" he begged. "Come over and help us!"

His plea was so earnest, and so insistent, that it sounded like the impassioned appeal of a desperately ill person for a doctor, or the craving of a student, totally lost and bewildered in his pursuit of knowledge, seeking the assistance of an approachable yet scholarly tutor.

It was a cry from the heart.

And it was also, to me, a clear sign from God.

Those distant hills of Macedonia that we had viewed only as misty outlines in the gathering dusk would have to be our next destination.

Early the following morning I shared my vision of the night before with Silas, Timothy and Luke, and all three of them agreed that God had shown us very definitely that we should make our way across to Macedonia.

Since we were all anxious to be on the move again, claiming a new land for our Lord, Luke, who had often told us of his visits to Greece in the course of his studies, was soon down at the harbour, consulting some of the sea captains whom he knew. And within hours he had arranged a passage for all four of us to Neapolis, the port of Philippi, in two days time!

What a thrill it was to embark upon this newest of challenges!

What eager anticipation tinged with just the slightest apprehension, and what animated conversation interspersed with short spells of silent reflection, there was on the ship as we anchored overnight in the lee of the island of Samothrace on our first and only night at sea. And as we set sail at daybreak next morning to complete our voyage to Macedonia the winds proved particularly favourable. It was almost as though God was pleased to see us set out, and had sent a special wind to hurry us along!

In mid-afternoon of the second day we slid silently in amongst the many vessels jostling for position in the harbour at Neapolis. There were no trumpets or fanfares as we stepped ashore, but our small party of four had arrived to bring the Good News to Europe.

We had no intention of stopping in the port of Neapolis, however.

Within hours of landing we were on the road again, and after a walk of some ten miles through a gradual pass in some gentle rolling hills and then out again on to an expansive plain, we arrived just before nightfall at our eventual destination, Philippi.

Having found ourselves somewhere to stop over for the night we settled down, tired after our journey, promising ourselves that we would spend the next few days finding our bearings, and exploring the city.

An interesting place it turned out to be, too.

Philippi was situated at almost the eastern extremity of the Via Egnatia, which was the road that the Romans had built from the Adriatic Sea to the Aegean, and because of its strategic position had been designated a Roman colony. That meant that there was a considerable Roman military presence in the city, and that it was governed by two magistrates appointed from the imperial capital. And as Luke took us on our first conducted tour around the local places of interest, beginning in the agora, the marketplace, we couldn't fail to notice the Roman influence everywhere. Although at least half of the population of the city were Greeks the Roman insignia flew from many buildings, Latin was spoken by many in the streets and shops, and even the coinage bore the imprint of the Caesar.

It was like Rome away from Rome, and Silas and I should have immediately felt at home. For we were Roman citizens.

When we were familiar with our new surroundings we then set about our next task, and that was finding a suitable location where we could most effectively begin to preach, teach, or even talk the Gospel, to someone from the city.

It had been easy in the past in cities where there had been a synagogue, but since Philippi was a predominantly military and agricultural, rather than commercial city, very few travelling merchant Jews had settled there. And since the laws of the Jewish nation stated that there must be 'at least ten wise men' residing in any settlement before a synagogue could be set up, there was no synagogue in Philippi.

After endless questions and exhaustive enquiries we discovered, however, that a number of Jewish women were meeting outdoors for prayer every Sabbath day, at a spot down by the river Gangites, about a mile outside the city.

This represented, I believed, our best opportunity to meet at least someone who would have at least some knowledge of the Holy Scriptures and some degree of respect for the one true God, in the midst of a city where anyone seemed to be able to worship any god they liked, at any time they liked, in whatever way they liked.

So on the Sabbath day we made our way down to the riverside, all four of us.

After having spent so many Sabbaths with no male company the few faithful women who met there were no doubt surprised to welcome four men all at once, but after we had introduced ourselves they were delighted to welcome us, and invited us to speak to them.

It was such a privilege to talk to these women about the Saviour. They were so keen, so attentive. Most of them were of Jewish extraction, and so I began, as I always endeavoured to do in such situations, by showing them from the Scriptures that Jesus Christ, who had been totally rejected by His own nation, was God's Anointed One, and that through faith in Him and in Him alone, we could be assured of everlasting peace.

One of the women in the group that first Sabbath was not a Jewess, we were to discover, but a well to do businesswoman from Thyatira in Asia. This lady, Lydia, had built up a prosperous business selling expensive designer clothing. There were many wealthy Greeks and Romans living in Philippi, and they were willing to pay great sums of money for Lydia's exclusive garment range. This consisted mainly of made-to-measure cloaks or togas, all woven in one piece without a seam, and dyed in the purple vats for which her hometown of Thyatira was famous.

Although the Sabbath day was like any other day in Philippi, I was initially quite surprised to find Lydia down by the riverside with the Jewish women. She must have been quite happy to shut up shop for the day, or perhaps leave someone else in charge, for she had, I was soon to detect, more important matters than making money on her mind.

She was a seeking soul.

As I presented the truth of the gospel by a combination of conversation and question and answer sessions, it was amazing to observe the manner in which she soaked up the meaning of the message. She was hanging on my every word.

Lydia had come from a heathen city, but had long since discovered that paganism could never satisfy the longings of her searching soul. She had found a measure of contentment with the Jewish women as they sought to worship the one true God, but yet she had found all the ceremonial of the Jewish law burdensome and incapable of affording her lasting peace.

When I continued to tell of Jesus and His love and His power to save and satisfy, Lydia trusted in Christ. God opened her heart to receive His Son as her Saviour. And we praised God that he had led us to Philippi, and our first convert in Europe!

Lydia had made it in business because of her belief in, and her ability to promote, her product. And when she became a Christian she began immediately to use that promotional enthusiasm for Christ. She found the peace she had been seeking for years, and she was determined to let everybody know about it!

In a matter of weeks two things had happened.

The first was that Lydia invited us along to her home to present the gospel message to her family and all the household servants, and as a result many of them were saved and baptized along with their mother and employer.

Lydia didn't settle either for having us just come to visit her in her grand home and then go away again to our less than luxurious lodgings. She insisted that since she had a big house, with more rooms than she could ever use, we should come and take up residence with her. I was against this at first, for I had always been one for maintaining my independence, making or mending a few tents to pay my way, but Lydia was not to be put off. She was a boss in business, was used to being obeyed, and just brushed aside any paltry excuses we tried to concoct. So Silas, Timothy, Luke and myself all moved into her house to be attended by her servants.

God who had opened Lydia's heart had also opened her home as well.

This turned out to be a good move, eventually, for it afforded us, in due course, a very acceptable base in which to establish our work, and from which to evangelise the city. And most of our original congregation lived there anyway!

For more than a month everything went well. God blessed our teaching and talking and a number of people, both men and women, turned to Christ.

I had always found, though, that when the work seemed to be prospering, that was the time it was most liable to be attacked, upset, or disrupted. And that is what happened at Philippi.

One Sabbath morning as we were making our way out of the city to go down to our outdoor 'house of prayer' by the riverside, a girl in her teens came running after us. She was dressed in a colourful flowing robe, and was well known in the city as a fortune-teller. Many idle Greek and Roman dignitaries, anxious to find what the future held for them, came to her masters and arranged a fortune-telling session. The clairvoyant teenager then predicted the client's fortune by her subtle demonic power, and her agents made their fortune out of it.

"These men are the servants of The Most High God!" the girl began to shriek. "They have come to show us the way of salvation!"

That morning she followed us most of the way down to the riverside, wailing all the way, before deciding eventually to return to her masters in the city.

Then during the week she saw us walking through the city streets and immediately began following us again, screaming in the same high-pitched voice, "These are the servants of the Most High God! They have come to show us the way of salvation!"

Everybody passing in the street just stopped and stared. For everybody knew that this girl was apt to work herself up into a frenzy. But many of them believed in her powers of prediction.

Eventually one afternoon I could endure it no longer. Silas and I had been out walking and were almost back at Lydia's house when it all began again behind us.

"These men are the servants of the Most High God! They have come to show us the way of salvation!"

Although what she said was correct, we were the servants of the Most High God, and we had come to show them the way of salvation, I could not bear to see the work of God promoted by such an evil agency. Turning round sharply, I fixed my eyes intently upon her and addressed the evil spirit within her.

"I command you in the name of Jesus Christ to come out of her!" I ordered.

All at once the shrill shrieking softened. She fell silent. The fierce, wild, faraway look died in her dark eyes. Within seconds she had returned to being a normal, sensible, and strangely attractive girl.

A marvellous transformation had occurred. Many of those who witnessed what had happened gazed in wonder at the former fortune-teller and listened with interest as we seized an ideal opportunity to tell them of the power of The Most High God, and the way of salvation.

Shortly afterwards, as we reasoned with the local people, the calm clairvoyant beside us serving as a very practical testimony to the extent of God's power, we could hear a commotion in the distance. It was not long either until we realized that the hullabaloo was heading in our direction.

Not everybody in the city was listening to us obviously. Some had sneaked off to tell the slave girl's masters of the radical change in their employee, which they were fully aware would effect a radical change in their earnings.

"Get them! Arrest them! They are nothing but troublemakers!" the angry agents were yelling.

Then unbelievably and almost instantly, the listening group around us was either transformed into or taken over by, a howling mob.

"To the magistrates!" they began to bawl. "To the magistrates!"

Neither of us was in a position to offer any resistance and in a short time we had been half carried half dragged before the two magistrates who were sitting in pomp to hear cases in the market place.

The magistrates sat in marble chairs on a raised dais. On either side of them stood Roman lictors, each carrying the axe and the bundle of rods that were the mark of Roman authority.

"What charge do you bring against these men?" one of the magistrates enquired.

"These fellows are wandering Jews and they are upsetting everything in this city!" one of the slave girl's former bosses claimed, taking great pains to conceal his main grievance. "They are expecting our people to take up and follow a set of alien customs that it would not be right for us to accept being Romans!"

Our accusers were very clever. They knew that at that time many Jews had been expelled from Rome, having been accused of inciting unrest. So what better case could they bring than that of subversive Jews?

Anxious to be seen to side with the crowd and the Roman authorities, the magistrates neither even questioned if the accusations were true nor gave either of us a chance to speak for himself, as they were required to do by the law they were supposed to be upholding.

One of the magistrates stood up, and looking across to his lictor, pronounced sentence.

"Flog them!" he commanded, and pointed down at us.

Then his companion did likewise.

Looking across at his lictor, who had already begun to untie his bundle of rods, he also gave sentence.

"Flog them!" he ordered, and pointed down at us.

Then the mob took it up.

"Flog them! Flog them! Flog them!" they bayed.

Chapter Fourteen

SONGS IN THE NIGHT

It would be pointless to protest.

We should have been able to claim immunity from public punishment on the grounds of our Roman citizenship. But even if we had been granted time to make the absolving statement, "I am a Roman citizen!" it would have made little or no difference in that highly charged, almost hysterical, atmosphere.

The Roman slaves who had surrounded us probably couldn't understand Greek, and our accusers who could understand it wouldn't want to hear it. And the magistrates certainly couldn't have heard it for the chaos all around.

Coarse clawing hands ripped our robes from our backs while we were being propelled by a series of vicious prods and punches to the whipping post. There our hands were tied to the post in the agora, and the lictors laid out their rods.

Although I had been attempting to brace myself for it, nothing really prepared me for the first lash across my back. A sting of pain shot through my body. Then I heard the swish of the second lictor's rod coming down on Silas, followed by an agonised intake of breath.

The lictors took it time about to lash us.

I winced in pain every time the supple rod came tearing into my back, and after the third or fourth stroke I could feel blood trickling down both of my sides.

Soon it was over.

The mob had been subdued into silence, whether by the severity of our sentence and suffering, or the satisfaction of seeing 'justice' done, I couldn't quite be sure. But I somehow suspected the latter.

The slaves who had ripped off our cloaks threw what remained of them roughly over our bleeding backs once more.

Then I heard, above the hubbub, one of the magistrates growling instructions to a Roman centurion.

"Escort these two agitators across to the prison and tell the jailer to keep them safely," he ordered. "They need to be taught a lesson or two!"

Having received an instruction like that the centurion and his soldiers showed us no favours as they force-marched us mercilessly across the thronging Via Egnatia and up towards the city prison on the lower slopes of the gentle hillside beyond.

I felt weak from the loss of blood and the shock of the beating, and probably the fact that I had just recently recovered from a severe bout of malaria didn't help to strengthen my shaking legs either.

Silas was slightly ahead of me, being bumped and butted along and I could see the huge dark bloodstains creeping across the back of his cloak. His back must be a sorry mess, I thought.

Yet the soldiers showed no concern for our condition.

Nor did the spectators care much for our feelings.

"So these are the servants of The Most High God!" someone mocked.

"And they have come to show us the way of salvation!" another across the road jeered back, amid gales of ribald laughter.

When we approached a square, squat building with thick windowless walls, I knew we had reached our destination.

The centurion passed the message of the magistrate on to the jailer.

"You are to keep these two rabble-rousers safe and show them no mercy!" he told him gruffly.

"Don't worry, I have just the right place for them!" the prison officer assured him.

It was the inner prison.

I felt like some heinous criminal as we were led past other convicted prisoners in the outer prison and then ushered into 'the right place' for us.

'The inner prison' was a very grand name for a dirty, dark, dank dungeon of a place, where the jangle of chains on the wrists of the other prisoners and their loud and incessant oaths and curses were the first sounds to greet us.

We were ordered to sit down and had each arm shackled at the wrist and the other end of the shackle chain was attached to a staple in the wall. Then our ankles were clamped firmly in the stocks.

When the jailer had satisfied himself that we would be 'safe' for the night he went out, pulling the huge, heavy door behind him, and dropping the bar that secured it in position, into place.

Suddenly all was dark. Pitch dark. There wasn't a light of any sort in that wretched, fetid place.

And it stank. Dreadfully.

Neither of us could bear to lie down, for our backs were so sore, and yet we realized that our God had placed us in that prison. We were there for Him, and we would use our time there to speak to Him in prayer, and exalt Him in praise. What else could we do?

What we were going through, was not to be compared in any way to what our Saviour had gone through for us. We were happy to be called upon to suffer for His sake.

As we prayed together I thanked God for guiding me to Silas as a companion on that mission. He had just proved to be a tower of strength in a howling storm. Many a lesser man would definitely have buckled under that beating.

Some of the uncouth and foul-mouthed men around us wanted to know what we had done to merit being confined in the inner prison, and we were more than pleased to tell them why we had come to Philippi, and why, after the saga of the slave girl, we had been beaten and detained.

As evening wore on into night one or two of the other prisoners, who were accustomed to the crude conditions, drifted off to sleep, but sleep was out of the question for either of us. We were too sore for one thing, and yet we wanted to praise God for sparing our lives, as well.

So we began to sing.

Silas and I had both been taught the Psalms of David from early boyhood so we took turns at calling out the opening words of a psalm, and then singing it together.

'He brought me up also out of a horrible pit, and out of the miry clay, and set my feet upon a rock and established my goings.

And he has put a new song in my mouth, even praise unto our God: many shall see it, and fear, and shall trust in the Lord...' we sang.

It soon became evident that we had an audience.

The many prisoners still awake had obviously never come across a couple of characters like us in their lives before. And we knew they were listening to us.

They had been moaning.

And now we were singing

They had been cursing their luck.

And now we were praising our God.

It was no problem to us to keep going.

'He brought them out of darkness and the shadow of death, and has broken their chains in pieces.

Oh that men would praise the Lord for his goodness and for his wonderful works to the children of men!' we went on.

'For he has broken the gates of brass, and cut through the bars of iron...'

It was almost midnight, and we were singing away quite happily, when the floor below us began to tremble. Then the trembling turned into a rocking. The sturdy walls of the prison began to shake, as though in fear. The staples fell away from between the stones and everybody's chains clanged to the floor.

"It's an earthquake!" somebody yelled in terror. "We are done for now!"

The stocks securing our ankles splintered and gaped open.

The pillars of the doorway writhed and twisted and the hinge-supports of the doors came loose. Then the bar across the outside of the door shivered and split.

The heavy door swung open with a crash.

When the earthquake had passed, the jailer came rushing down to the prison. Looking out from the darkness of my dungeon I could see him silhouetted in the moonlight in the opening that had once held the outer door. It was now lying off at a crazy angle behind him

I realised immediately what he was going to do. When he saw the wreck of the prison he assumed that his charges would all have escaped. The glint of the drawn sword in the moonlight was my clue.

"Don't harm yourself! We are all here!" I shouted.

Possibly reassured by my intervention he called out, "Torches! Torches!" and when a pair of slaves had rushed up beside him with flaming torches he came across, through the outer prison to the dungeon where his high-risk prisoners were detained.

Our singing had long since ceased, and we had been glad to stand up and stretch our stiff legs, ease our aching bones, and change the painful position of our backs which were by then a matted mass of torn flesh and congealed black blood.

The flickering torches cast eerie shadows around that scene of devastation, but it was at once obvious that the jailer had other matters on his mind by then. The man who had been charged with keeping us safely arrived trembling at our feet!

Then, when he had regained his composure sufficiently, he invited us to step out and join him in the wider expanse of the outer prison. By that time many of the prisoners were on their feet, and most of his family and household staff had swarmed in from his personal residence at the prison gate.

Quite a crowd had gathered in the shambles which had once served as the city prison when the terrified prison officer looked across at us and asked, "Sirs, what must I do to be saved?"

He had probably heard of our preaching, or possibly of the slave girl's proclamation, and when the earthquake had alerted him to what he would have considered the wrath of the gods, he realized that there must be some meaning to our message.

And we were only too happy to answer his question.

"Believe on the Lord Jesus Christ and you will be saved," we told him, and then Silas and I went on to explain the way of salvation to the hastily gathered, but nonetheless attentive, audience.

The jailer trusted in Christ as soon as the gospel, in all its fullness was explained to him. And so also did each member of his family, and all his household servants, before that night was out.

What had happened in the life of the lady Lydia also occurred in the life and experience of this formerly rough Roman prison officer.

When he became a believer in the Lord Jesus Christ he became a most hospitable person! The man had become a completely changed character!

After ensuring that all the other prisoners were as secure as he could possibly make them in the circumstances, he invited us across into his home.

The jailer's wife, who had also heard us speak, and had trusted in Christ, brought a basin of warm water. It was a marvellous triumph for the gospel, I thought, as the man who, only eight or ten hours before had bundled us into the inner prison, began tenderly detaching our blood-soaked cloaks from our blood-caked backs. When he had this done he bathed our wounds carefully and poured healing and soothing oil all over them.

What a relief that was! It was certainly the first token of tender loving care we had experienced from a human for some time!

Then, with our strength in some measure restored, Silas and I baptised each and every individual who had trusted in Christ.

We had come to Philippi to show them the way of salvation, and when it seemed that our mission was coming to an unfortunate and unfruitful end, God in His wisdom had overruled and many had come to accept Jesus Christ, personally, as their Saviour.

Everyone was rejoicing in his or her newly found faith. Nobody ever thought about going back to bed, and much less about going to sleep.

It was so exciting!

But we were also so hungry!

The jailer and his wife offered us a meal and it was wonderful just to refresh our hungry weary bodies with food in the presence of so many eager new Christians. The night passed quickly, as we told them more about the truths of the faith, of how we ourselves had been saved, of our travels and labours for the Lord, and of the infant church in Lydia's house.

Day had just spread its mantle of light over the cracked and crumbling city, and many of its residents were making the most of the opportunity to assess the extent of the damage, when we heard voices outside.

Our host went out to investigate and he came back in five minutes with a broad grin on his face.

"That is two of the lictors out there," he began. "They have come from the magistrates to order me to let you two men go. Isn't that good news? You are now free men! The magistrates must have been scared of the earthquake, too. They probably thought their gods were punishing them for punishing you! But sure it doesn't matter. Our God has overruled. You are now free to go!"

"But we will not be going," I replied softly.

The smile of delight on the jailer's face suddenly vanished and was immediately replaced by a frown of disbelief.

"What do you mean?" he enquired, completely bamboozled.

"Send those messengers in to me, and you will soon find out what I mean," I told him.

When he had complied with my request, and the two court emissaries were brought in to where we were, I said to them, "You go back and tell those magistrates that we are both Roman citizens and yet they have beaten us openly, without even giving us any chance of a fair trial and they have thrown us into prison without anything ever being proven against us. And do they think for one minute that they are going to get rid of us secretly? No way! We are going back into the prison now and if they want us out they can come themselves and escort us out!"

With that I signalled to Silas and he and I thanked the rather bemused jailer and his wife for their kindness and care, and returned to the prison.

And within minutes the lictors had set off with my ultimatum to the magistrates.

I had no doubt but that we would hear from them soon again! For if the slightest whimper of what they had done ever reached Rome they would certainly be in danger of losing their jobs, at least.

During our sit-in I explained my action to Silas.

I would be happy to leave Philippi, I told him, and in fact it would probably be best for everybody if both of us did. But for the sake of the suddenly substantially boosted group of Christians we were leaving behind, it was important that we didn't leave under any sort of a cloud of suspicion. We couldn't be seen to slink out of the city as criminals who had escaped their sentence by sneaking out of prison after an earthquake. It was essential for posterity that we left as honourable Roman citizens, with our names cleared and our testimony before God and men intact.

He soon saw the wisdom of my thinking, and we hadn't long to wait either to be vindicated.

Before mid-morning the two magistrates arrived right down in the inner prison, accompanied by our friend the new-Christian jailer.

They were ever so apologetic and consented to escort us out of the prison, thus clearing us of our sentence. They did, however, also request that we leave the city as soon as possible for they argued that if we remained it would mean further trouble for us, and our 'followers' as they described them, and undoubtedly for them.

We agreed to this, but there were one or two matters we had to attend to before we left.

The first of these was to introduce the prison officer and his family to the believers who by then had begun to meet regularly in Lydia's spacious home, and another was to discuss our next move, and our next destination with Luke and Timothy.

After a period of prayer and consultation we decided that Timothy should accompany Silas and myself to Thessalonica, but that Luke should remain behind. With his professional standing, his Greek nationality, and thorough knowledge of Greek culture he would be readily accepted in the local community and could prove a tremendous help in overseeing the establishment of the infant church.

Early next morning we set out, and it was a curious mix of people who gathered in Lydia's house, and spilled out into the courtyard, just to bid us farewell.

There was the landlady we were leaving, a wealthy business-woman from Asia, fussing around over all the last minute arrangements.

There was a poor Greek slave girl, who up until a few days before had owned nothing, not even herself. She had changed the flamboyant robe of a fortune-teller for the simple garment of a servant, but the radiant smile on her settled face gave notice that something else had changed as well.

And right at the front of the crowd was a Roman jailer. This man had swapped the coarse cruelty of his occupation for the loving care of a Christian in one God-appointed meeting at midnight!

'Come over into Macedonia and help us!" the man from Macedonia had begged.

Although two out of the three of us were still nursing stiff and tender backs from our public flogging, all of our minds were focussed and our hearts praising God as we stepped out on to the busy Via Egnatia to head westward.

We had seen more than men 'helped' through faith in Christ in Macedonia already.

And we were bound for its capital, Thessalonica.

Chapter Fifteen

TURNING THE WORLD UPSIDE DOWN!

It was a hundred miles to Thessalonica and the journey took us almost five days.

We made an overnight stop in Amphipolis and another in Apollonia, but I did not feel any necessity to linger long in either of those locations. Neither of those towns, though important trading centres, had a synagogue, or any other centre where we could commence to contact the local people. We had gathered from other travellers, however, that there was a flourishing Jewish community and a large synagogue in Thessalonica, and so it was to that city that we pushed forward with all possible speed.

When we arrived in the Macedonian capital we discovered it to be a completely different city from the one which we had just recently been asked to leave.

Philippi had been a Roman colony.

Thessalonica was a 'free' city.

Philippi had been governed by two magistrates, appointed from Rome.

Thessalonica had its own team of seven locally appointed rulers, called 'politarchs', who had the power of life and death over its citizens.

Since it had been declared a free city by the Romans, they had guaranteed that there would be no military garrison within its gates. We found it surprising, then, and a complete contrast to Philippi, to walk in along the Via Egnatia and see barely a soldier in sight!

And there wasn't even a single sign of the insignia of Roman office on display anywhere, either.

Our initial impression of Thessalonica was of an extremely prosperous city, ideally situated to make the best of every commercial opportunity. It had a very busy harbour bringing in both goods and visitors from other lands, and it was on the great east-west road that the Romans had built, and this combination no doubt contributed to the fact that it was constantly booming and buzzing with business.

It will be interesting, I thought, as we walked around searching for an address I had been given, to see how the citizens of this 'free' city react to the news of free salvation, through faith in the crucified Christ.

Although I was anxious to begin presenting the Good News to the thousands of Thessalonians, there were two practical matters which I thought it important to resolve as soon as possible.

And the first was to find somewhere to stay. I had been told that a far-out relative of mine called Jason now lived in Thessalonica, and after asking many questions and taking a few wrong turns we eventually found his house.

When I had told Jason who I was, and had introduced Silas my partner, and Timothy 'my son', to him, I asked about the possibility of finding reasonable accommodation in the city.

"Don't worry about finding anywhere else. You can all stay with me, I have a big enough place here," Jason volunteered.

We thanked God for that! It was great to realize that our God had gone before us, and had prepared us somewhere to stay.

And so, with the issue of finding somewhere to live out of the way, our only other, and potentially long-term problem, was to find something to live on. Jason had been very kind, but we couldn't just expect to stay with him for nothing, and we needed money to buy food in the city's many markets.

To provide us with a rather meagre, and not even very regular, but at least better than nothing sort on an income, I used my trade training from Tarsus to set myself up as a part-time tentmaker, both making and mending tents.

We had not come to that bustling city as either traders or tourists, however.

We had come as lights to the Gentiles, to tell them of Jesus and His love.

So it possibly seemed peculiar that in such a populous Greek city we should begin our mission in the Jewish synagogue, but this was an approach that had worked before, so we decided to adopt it again. At least the Jews and proselytes in the synagogue recognised and reverenced the God we had come to proclaim. And that gave us a sound basis on which to begin.

For three successive Sabbath days we taught in the synagogue. There was a tremendous interest in what we had to say as we proved from the scriptures that the Messiah must come to suffer before He comes to reign. We sought to show that He had already come to earth in the person of Jesus of Nazareth, and that He had come with the express purpose of dying on the cross to take away the sin of the world. It gave me no difficulty, either, to prove from the scriptures, and from my own personal experience that Jesus had risen from the dead, and that He would still come as the all-conquering King, the Messiah as the Jews expected Him.

In the meantime, however, Jesus was enlisting men and women from earth to His kingdom by inviting them to believe in Him, and in return for this belief they would immediately be freed from the penalty and punishment of their sin and the limitations of the law, and be given eternal salvation.

There were many interesting discussions. There were many animated, and on occasions almost acrimonious, question and answer sessions, led by the local rabbis.

This good news of peace and joy in believing was something the synagogue congregations had never heard voiced before, and many came out of curiosity to hear it, and many trusted in Christ.

Before we arrived in the city, those attending worship in the synagogue every Sabbath were comprised of a core group of staunch and traditional Jews, as I had once been myself, and a much larger group of searching Greeks. These were people who had become disillusioned with the pagan worship of the legendary gods of the Greeks, such as Zeus and Aphrodite, and who had found some semblance of satisfaction and reality in embracing the concept of the one Almighty God of the Jews.

As we reasoned for those first three weeks, a few of the Jews trusted in the Saviour, and one of these men, Aristarchus, was to prove a real stalwart in the years to come. Our visit to Thessalonica would have been worth it for Aristarchus alone! But he wasn't alone, for in those early days of our visit, Jason, our host, and my relative, was saved as well.

If there was a trickle of blessing amongst the Jewish community in the city, however, there was a torrent amongst the proselytes and the God-fearing Greeks.

What happened among them was little short of a revival!

Dozens of enquiring Greeks, who had heard us speak in the synagogue initially, began to come up to Jason's home to talk with us, and hear more about Jesus. There were times when Silas, Timothy and I were all kept busy, talking to somebody, so much so that we stopped going to the synagogue on the Sabbath and began to do all our preaching and teaching in the streets and in our lodgings. I spent many profitable days there, working away, cutting and stitching tent cloth, and talking and teaching away, about Jesus and new life in Him.

And many who came to talk about Jesus went away trusting in Him.

It was wonderful, a mighty movement of God!

It was fantastic, too, to witness the number of the leading women of the city, some of them the wives of leading dignitaries, who believed the message. They had been mildly interested in, but not utterly devoted to, the Jewish religion, but when we came along, preaching a Gospel with no difficult doctrines, no national exclusion clauses, and no endless and apparently pointless ceremonials, they were immediately attracted to it.

When they discovered also that simple faith in Christ brought with it the twin blessings of peace with God and everlasting life and that both these free gifts came with a Divine guarantee, they were more than happy to trust in Him. And they found happiness, such as they had never known before, through doing so.

Those were encouraging days in more ways than one.

For in addition to seeing so many open their hearts to the Lord I was thrilled one afternoon, when sewing away at a tent I had almost finished, and sowing the Gospel seed in further fertile hearts, I received a small group of tired travellers.

What a joy it was to see them!

I recognised them immediately!

This dust-covered delegation was from Philippi, and had come, they said, to bring us a 'small gift of money as a token of their love, to help with our expenses.'

And how welcome that was! There was a famine in the country at that time and Timothy and Jason had both been complaining that the price of bread in the city markets, when you could find it at all, was about six times what it would normally have been.

My tent making could provide us with a basic living at basic prices but it had never been a marvellous money-spinner.

Now, through the grace of our God in stirring the hearts of His children we had enough to see us through the crisis comfortably.

And when our brethren arrived back in Philippi they must have conveyed either the nature of our bordering on the breadline circumstances, or our delight at their thoughtfulness and generosity to the Christians in the growing church there for they repeated their kind action.

In a month's time, a second gift arrived.

What a provision for our need, from God who had undertaken to supply all my need when I first set out in His service!

But when all seemed to be going well, and God was blessing our ministry, and it seemed that people were turning to the Lord almost on a daily basis, everything changed. This was nothing new for us. We had grown accustomed to it.

The leaders of the synagogue had become aggrieved on two counts. They were annoyed with themselves that they had been unable to refute our 'heretical' teaching that a crucified carpenter from a poor family could be the promised Messiah, and they were angry that so many of their former adherents had been so deluded as to believe it. For the numbers attending synagogue worship had decreased in direct proportion to the increased numbers flocking to Jason's home, and other city venues to hear us!

Thus they decided to do something about it, and began by commencing a whispering campaign against us among all the local idlers who whiled away their tedious days either in the marketplace or down by the harbour, vainly searching for anything that could in any sense of the word be termed 'excitement'.

When the Jews told them of this trio of itinerant preachers who had come to stay at Jason's house, and who were teaching a false religion about a king who was planning to set up in opposition to the Emperor, many of those layabouts who as a general rule cared nothing about any religion of any sort, decided to take the law into their own hands.

Late one afternoon when all three of us were out of the house an unruly mob arrived outside the door of our lodgings screaming for us. However when they discovered that we weren't at home they dragged Jason, Aristarchus and some of the others down before the politarchs and presented the city rulers with a problem. These men were well aware that Jason and his friends were honest law-abiding citizens, yet they knew that if they were to maintain law and order in their city they had somehow to be seen to satisfy the demands of the mob before them

Some of them had heard of this foreign religion from their wives who had recently become Christians and were seemingly every happy in it and with it, and yet they couldn't afford to antagonise the powerful Jewish community.

So they reached a compromise, and it was a very fearful Jason who relayed their decision to us later that evening.

"I'm sorry, brothers, but you will have to leave Thessalonica as soon as possible," he began, obviously shaken by his experiences. "I have been bound over to keep the peace in the city, and have also been asked to make sure that you leave here as soon as possible. It would really be better if you went now, tonight, for your own safety.

The city leaders were able to calm that crowd today, but I doubt if they could do it again. The man who accused you before the politarchs portrayed you as a group of rebel reactionaries who were turning the world upside down, causing trouble wherever you went! And since they feel a bit cheated at not having been successful in bringing you to justice, I hate to think what would happen if they were to get their hands on any of you, especially you, Paul!"

Turning the world upside down indeed!

I liked it!

A sick little Jew, who had to take a part-time job to help pay his expenses, his faithful friend, and a nineteen year old, turning the world upside down!

There was nobody could turn the world upside down except the God who had made it, and He was doing it, through us, His humble servants.

But Jason was right. We would have to go, and soon.

It didn't take long for us to collect our few belongings and prepare for yet another hasty retreat from yet another sinister situation.

Where though, could we go?

There were three choices.

We could go down to the harbour and try to book a passage back to Troas, but I didn't want to do that. I wanted to go forward with the Gospel, not back. Or we could return to Philippi, where the Christians who had been so kind to us would undoubtedly be glad to see us again, but some city officials might not be quite so overjoyed. Alternatively we could press on westward, and that is what we felt God was guiding us to do.

So just after midnight we were on our way again, stealing through the deserted streets, under the triumphal Arch of Augustus, and out through the western gate.

It was difficult that first night on an unknown road in the darkness, but when we reckoned that we were far enough away from the city to be safe we were able to rest until morning. Then after two days travel we reached our destination, Berea.

As 'a city of refuge' Berea proved to be an excellent choice. It was a pleasant place with streamlets flowing in the streets, but its main advantage was that it was some miles off the main Via Egnatia, and therefore much quieter than either Philippi or Thessalonica.

And we were to be pleasantly surprised by our reception in the synagogue there, too!

When I presented to them from the Psalms, and from prophecies like those of Isaiah and Habakkuk, the message about a Messiah who was destined to die, be buried and rise again, and about faith in Him as the sole means of salvation, I was pleased to find that they didn't reject it immediately, or angrily. They proved open-minded enough to spend time studying the scriptures to probe into the matter for themselves, and it became almost an obsession for some of them. They didn't wait until the Sabbath to do their searching. They were at it every day, reading, comparing, enquiring.

And again many of them, including many of the influential ladies in the town, came to trust in Christ.

We ought to have known, too, that this run of unopposed blessing was too good to last, and so it proved.

However they heard, I could never manage to find out, whether it was with Jewish traders travelling between the towns, or whether some agitator from Thessalonica had decided to track us down, the Jewish authorities in that city discovered our whereabouts, and vowed not to rest until they had wrecked the work in Berea, too.

When some of the new converts who had been so keen to search the scriptures, and so happy to believe in the Lord Jesus, heard of the rent-a-mob unrest being threatened by the Jewish leaders, they quickly came to the conclusion that it would not be wise for me to remain in Berea. Although Silas and Timothy would still be relatively safe there, it was reckoned that my life could be seriously endangered if I overstayed.

So I had to be on the move again.

Although half-heartedly offering to set out on my own I was glad when the Berean believers insisted that a number of them would accompany me, wherever I went. They needed to be with me for protection, to act as my bodyguards, they maintained, as well as acting as my medical attendants in the absence of Doctor Luke who was still preaching and practising back in Philippi. I was, they kept telling me, too weak to make a long journey alone. And I didn't argue.

It was good to travel with such a group of keen new Christians for I was able to instruct them on the journey. When we had made our way down to the coast, two of my escorts arranged a passage to Athens, the Greek capital, where they knew I would be safe from jealous Jews, and for three balmy days we sailed southwards over a calm blue sea.

It was in the cool of the early morning of the fourth day at sea that we nudged into the busy harbour at Piraeus, the port of Athens.

Looking up from the harbour I could see the rays of the rising sun glowing red on the pillars of the Parthenon, high up on the Acropolis.

My companions stayed with me on the last leg of my journey up into the city and until they had helped me to procure lodgings. Then they set off back down to the harbour. They reckoned that if they asked around they might just come across a boat sailing northwards again before nightfall.

As they were about to disappear around a street corner they turned to wave and I called after them, "Make sure you tell Silas and Timothy to come down to me here as soon as possible!"

And with that they turned the corner, and were gone.

I had been left alone for the first time in years.

And I had been left alone in Athens.

Chapter Sixteen

JESUS AND ANASTASIS

What a contrast Athens proved to be to anywhere I had ever visited before!

As I strolled through the crowded streets of the capital of Greece, which also claimed to be the cultural capital of the world, I was shocked at the extent of the idol worship all around.

This city was reckoned to be so advanced and so enlightened, and yet to me it looked so backward and so dark!

Around every corner I turned there seemed to be yet another altar to yet another god. The place was crammed with temples, shrines, altars and images. They were absolutely everywhere.

In the course of those first few lonely days as I tried to find my way around, I witnessed a wide variety of people presenting a wide variety of sacrifices before a wide variety of shrines in an attempt to curry favour with a wide variety of gods.

I felt so sorry for them. These were people of such intellectual prowess involved in a display of total spiritual darkness.

It was sickening for it was nothing other than a pathetic demonstration of educated ignorance.

Although my friends had not yet responded to my call for help from Macedonia, and I often felt isolated, I was never absolutely alone. For my God was with me, and my faith in Him gave me the strength to go on. The more I saw of the host of futile, distant deities all around, the more I considered myself blessed to be the servant of the omnipotent, yet eminently approachable God of both creation and salvation.

On my first two Sabbaths in the city I followed my well-established pattern of approach in any new location, by attending the local synagogue, and when invited to speak, told all present of Christ, the Messiah. The congregation listened with obvious interest to what I had to say but since the Jews were a small, and very much a minority group in the city, however, I felt that their fervour for the ancient faith, if they ever had any, had probably been diluted by the widespread worthless worship all around. Their response to the message of the gospel as I brought it forth from the sacred scriptures was more apathetic than antagonistic. They weren't rushing to trust in Christ, but then they weren't rushing to raise a riot either, and I suppose that was always something.

The synagogue was only one of hundreds of places of worship in Athens, and would be very near the bottom of the list of popular places to visit in the city, so I soon gathered that it was not going to serve as a launching pad for an effective strike on enemy territory.

There was only one way to present the gospel in the city of Athens, I decided, and that was by meeting the inquisitive and argumentative Athenians in the market place and engaging them in discussion.

The agora was at the hub of city life. Nearly everything happened in, around or near it. In the main marketplace itself, and in some of the streets running off it, there were a multitude of shops and stalls selling everything from cheese and olives, to earthenware jars and glass dishes, and even parchment, vellum and wax tablets for the many students thronging around. Slaves sat sweating in the searing sun on a raised platform in one corner. They were simply waiting for the auctioneer to knock them down to the highest bidder.

As I mingled with the people under the welcome shade of the plane trees, I began to talk to some of the philosophical idlers who frequented the nerve centre of the city. These pseudo-intellectuals spent all day, every day, just hearing, discussing, accepting, rejecting or endlessly debating some novel idea or introduction in art, literature or religion.

It was slow, uphill work.

Some days a good crowd gathered around me and a lively discussion took place as I told them of the one true God, and His Son, Jesus Christ. On other days I was most discouraged, for it seemed that I was making little or no headway at all.

Towards the end of my second week in Athens my whole being was given one tremendous boost. I had just returned to my lodgings at dusk when I heard voices, which I was sure I recognized, outside.

Could it possibly be?

I rushed out into the street. And yes. It was.

Silas and Timothy had been given my invitation, or perhaps it was an instruction, to come to me as soon as possible. And they had done just that. They had come post-haste to find me.

We were all so happy to be together again, and talked far into the night.

I had so many questions to ask. After all, I hadn't seen the face of a friend, or heard the prayer of a believer for almost two weeks! It had been awful!

Could I possibly get back to Macedonia, which I loved so much, and where God had so blessed our labours for Him? was the first thing I wanted to know.

The answer to that one, both Silas and Timothy agreed, would have to be No.

The Jews in Thessalonica were still stirring up all sorts of trouble for the Christians in the city, and if I were to return it could only make things worse for them, not better.

"They would kill you, too, Paul, if they could only catch you, I'm sure," Timothy ended by remarking earnestly. I loved his honest eyes and his youthful ardour.

That was disappointing. In truth I had just been biding my time in Athens until I could return to Macedonia, and now that appeared to be out.

It was after a period of prayer, and sometime in the early hours of the next morning, that we worked out our next plan of action. We decided that Timothy, young though he was, should return to Thessalonica to encourage the Christians there, and that Silas, who was second only to myself on the Jewish hit list in that city, should pass through quietly to Philippi, and bring me news from there.

We spent the next day chatting together as I showed my two dear friends around the idol-strewn city in which I was going to have to remain, and then early on the second morning they bade me 'Goodbye' and set out for the harbour at Piraeus to book a passage back to Macedonia.

Now I was alone in Athens. Again. It had been marvellous to renew friendship with Timothy and Silas, but how I missed them when they left!

One morning I stood staring up at the architectural magnificence of the Parthenon, while counting up something in my head.

It was, I calculated, more than eight years since Barnabas and I had set out for Cyprus, with young Mark in tow, and since that time I had travelled hundreds, perhaps even thousands of miles, but I had never, at any time, been without at least one travelling companion. How I enjoyed the constant company and Christian courage of like-minded men.

But now I was on my own, again.

How long would it be before I saw another friendly face, this time? I wondered.

God, I knew, was planning my programme, however, and I placed myself into His gracious hands. It was all I could do.

There was nothing else for it but to return to the teaching in the agora, until either Timothy and Silas returned, or my Heavenly Father directed otherwise.

By that time some of the local philosophers had begun stopping to question me, often scornfully, about my beliefs.

There were, I was to discover from talking to them, two distinct schools of thought amongst the thinkers of Athens. The Epicureans and The Stoics, as they were known, had differing ideas about the origin and meaning of life.

The Epicureans believed that the world in which they lived just happened by chance, appearing somehow from nowhere, and they doubted the existence of any deity of any kind. They maintained that it was important to be happy in life. People should seek to gratify their own desires, and seek their own pleasure, whatever the cost. Theirs was basically an 'eat drink and be merry, for tomorrow we die', philosophy.

The Stoics, on the other hand, believed that there was a God of a kind, out there, somewhere, but no one could know, feel, or experience Him in any personal way. He was present in anything that had life, such as birds, trees, animals, flowers, or fish and if you cared to worship Him you could do so as you pleased. It was a vague impersonal pantheism. Virtue, to them, was life's most important quality. People should seek to live an honourable life, devoid of showing emotion, which was interpreted as demonstrating weakness. Stoics treated pain and pleasure just the same, endeavouring to keep 'a stiff upper lip' at all times. And if life became too much for anybody they believed that it was courageous, possibly even commendable, to escape by suicide.

There was only one point on which there seemed to be general agreement between these Athenian apologists and that was on the subject of death. To both the Epicureans and the Stoics, death ended everything. You lived, you died and you were finished. That was it. Full stop. No more.

The concept of a life after death, in either a resurrected body or some sort of an eternal, spiritual state was totally foreign to their thinking. They had never even considered such a possibility, before.

When I began to teach about Jesus, and His resurrection from the dead, therefore, they were very scathing.

"What is this seed–picker saying?" they jeered, using the illustration of a second-rate rambling philosopher who picks up odd snippets from here and there to form them into some weird and wonderful theory of his own.

"He seems to be trying to introduce a couple of new gods to us," another remarked more thoughtfully. "He keeps talking about Jesus and Anastasis."

This showed me just how spiritually blind these people were, and how little they had bothered to try to understand of what it was that I had actually been trying to tell them! For well over three weeks I had been talking to them about Jesus, how that He had been crucified at Calvary, back in Jerusalem, and how that He had been buried and had risen again from the dead. Jesus and the resurrection had been the main plank of my platform with them, every day.

Now these people, who were little more than the scorned 'seed-pickers' themselves, had come to the conclusion that I had been presenting two new gods to them, one of whom was called Jesus, and the other, his cohort, called Anastasis, 'the Resurrection'!

One afternoon I was teaching away as usual when a number of the leading men from the Council of Areopagus, the body which controlled all matters of religion and education in the city, came across to where I was sitting. I had noticed them in the group standing around, but had paid no attention at first. They had possibly been contacted by some of the plentiful philosophers in the city, or perhaps they had heard me speak themselves, but in any event I was glad of the opportunity they afforded me.

"Would you like to come up to Mar's Hill and explain this new teaching of yours to us?" they invited. "You are propagating some strange ideas and we would just like to hear what it is all about."

I was happy to follow them out of the bustling agora and up the steep slope towards Mars Hill, a rocky outcrop, overlooking the city. They led the way, and I followed up the sixteen shiny steps, which brought us up to their outdoor courtroom. These steps had been carved out of the rock, and were worn smooth by the passage of thousands of former feet.

When I arrived up on the top of the Hill with its jutting rocks forming makeshift seats, I discovered that I wasn't by any means alone. There were some serious looking elderly judges already seated on the most prominent seats. A number of other Athenians, mostly men, sat around at various points where they could see and hear what was going on, but from where also, if they ever became bored with the proceedings, they could gaze down over the city.

It was another ten minutes before anything could happen for when some of my agora audience heard that I had been asked to speak before the Council, they followed me up. They must obviously have been spreading the news, too, as they came, for a steady stream of local idlers, and wealthy businessmen and artisans with their retinue of servants, kept pouring from the narrow opening at the top of the steps and then fanning out to take a seat wherever they could find one. So whenever it was time for court to commence this most accessible of public galleries was packed.

At last everyone seemed settled and when asked once more to give a thorough explanation of my 'strange teaching' I stood up, and looked around, before beginning.

I was right in the heart of a city steeped in paganism. Up behind me, shining white on the summit of the Acropolis was the Parthenon, easily the most impressive Temple in the city. The Temple of Mars was almost beside me, and the sanctuary of Eumenides immediately below. Also below was the teeming agora, with streets leading off it in all directions and every street dotted with idols of all sorts.

The blue sky, the canopy of my God, was above.

Rabbi Gamaliel had often told us, back in the House of Interpretation, that we should always approach an unknown audience courteously, and we should always try, wherever possible, to establish a point of contact, however remote, with our listeners. I had never forgotten that, and I tried to put it into practice that day on Mars Hill.

Having surveyed the scene, I began.

"Athenians!" I said, stretching out my hand, "I have observed that in every respect you are unusually religious. You desire to pay homage to all the gods, and neglect none. In fact every day on my way up to the agora I pass a white marble altar inscribed TO THE UNKNOWN GOD. Well, it is that God, whom you worship, without knowing anything about, that I have come to present to you."

I could judge from the reaction of some that I had been successful in establishing my point of contact, and yet I had also informed them that I hadn't arrived in their city to introduce another new god, for they had gods enough already. I had come to tell them more about the one true God, whom many of them were subconsciously seeking.

With everyone apparently listening, I then set forth the nature of the God I worshipped. Sweeping my arm around to encompass the dozens of temples dotted all over their city, I informed them that my

God had created everything, and so didn't need to dwell in any edifice, however ornate, that men would choose to make.

Having presented God as creator of all things I went on to portray Him as also the provider of all things for mankind. It was God who gave us our life, our food, and everything required for daily existence. I knew it was important to show God, not as some distant deity, but as near and accessible, so I quoted from Aratus, a Greek poet, who, like myself, had been born in Cilicia, and whose work I had read years before in Tarsus.

"As certain of your own poets have said, " I told them, "'We are also his offspring.'"

Some of the learned judges in the seats of privilege raised an interested eyebrow when I began to quote their poetry.

Perhaps this man is more than just a wandering Jewish intellectual outcast, I could almost see them thinking.

It was now time to bring my audience to the main point of my message, and help further my primary purpose in life. I had so far told them of God the creator and provider of all things. Now I had to lead on to giving them a clear explanation of Jesus and the resurrection. These people should be left in no doubt that my God had sent His Son to be their Saviour.

"Since we are God's offspring," I went on, "it is a mistake to suppose that He can be represented by idols or images, no matter how cleverly they are crafted by the art or imagination of man in gold, silver, or stone. We are beyond that now. The times of that old ignorance God has overlooked but now He commands all men everywhere to repent and turn to Him, for He has set a day when He will judge the world in righteousness by that Man whom He has ordained. And God has provided proof of this to everyone by raising Him from the dead..."

Suddenly hoots of derision arose.

I had just come to the point where I was about to proclaim Christ as the Saviour of mankind, when my audience erupted in ridicule.

"The resurrection, indeed! Listen to him!" they hissed. "What nonsense!"

Then the crowd, who had been so attentive during the earlier part of my speech, began to stir.

"Come on!" I could hear them calling to each other. "We're not listening to any more of that rubbish!" And they began to rise and walk away.

Suddenly the stream of people who had earlier fanned out to cover the open-air auditorium had become a laughing line of people waiting to descend the narrow steps and disappear. I was soon going to be left forsaken, once more. And the prospect was sickening. I felt I had really let both my Saviour and myself down in a big way this time.

"We will hear you again on this matter sometime," a couple of the council leaders tried to console me, but I suspected that these were just empty words designed to soften the blow of outright rejection.

My audience was in full retreat by then, giggling together and shouting back over their shoulders some of them, "Raised from the dead, indeed! The man's mad!"

I went back to my room desperately disappointed.

What was I going to do now?

My message had been laughed out of court and I felt deserted by all but God.

It took me a few days before I felt I could show my face in the agora again, but when I did it was to receive a pleasant surprise.

A philosopher who had been one of my most ardent opponents came up to me and asked, "Did you see Dionysius from the council? He has been looking for you for days."

Wondering if this was perhaps another summons to appear before the Areopagus I made a few enquiries and found the said Dionysius.

And what news he had for me! What he had wanted to see me about had nothing to do with arranging another meeting. It was to tell me that he had heard me speak in the agora and on Mars Hill and had trusted in Christ! Then later that day I was to hear of Damaris, a servant girl who had been on Mars Hill. She too had become a Christian.

So God had sent two radiant rays of encouragement to pierce through the deep darkness of my despair. My stay in Athens hadn't been a complete and utter disaster, after all. God had worked in the city, and had brought at least two souls to Himself.

But I couldn't stay there any longer.

Nobody bothered with me in the market place any more.

To a fiery faith like mine this complete indifference to the gospel was more difficult to accept than outright opposition. It would never have crossed the cultured minds of those civilized Athenians to stone me, or beat me. They were much too educated for that. They just ignored me completely. And their cold disdain cut into me more deeply than the stones of a mob or the lictor's rods had ever done!

There must be other dark places in this wicked world where God could use me to beam forth the light of the gospel of Jesus Christ to other more responsive Gentiles.

Within days I had heard of one possibility and made up my mind to try it.

Having spent some time in impassioned prayer about this contemplated move, I left instructions with my host to send Silas and Timothy after me when they came, and packed up my few belongings and set out from Athens a weak and disconsolate man. The blistering heat of the city had only served to leave me feeling sick and tired, and the freezing cold of my spiritual reception had left me feeling almost, but not entirely, a failure.

From the harbour at Piraeus I boarded a ship making the short passage westward across the Saronic Gulf to Cenchrea, the eastern port of Corinth.

How would I fare in that city of sin? was my next concern.

Chapter Seventeen

NOBODY'S GOING TO HURT YOU!

When the Acrocorinth, a great cone of a hill sticking up straight and sheer a thousand feet or so above the plain below, came into view, I assumed that I was approaching my destination.

As I drew nearer, I could see, like a crown placed deftly on the head of this hill, the Temple of Venus, which, I had been told, housed a thousand 'priestesses', who though always distinctive for they were dressed in white, helped spread evil and immorality through the city nestling below.

If Athens, which I had not really been awfully sorry to leave, could be regarded as the cultural capital of that region of Greece, then Corinth, which I was just about to enter, was, in a strange combination, both its commercial and recreational capital.

Situated as it was, on a narrow strip of land between the shipping routes of the Aegean and the Adriatic, Corinth had become a natural concourse for sailors and traders of every nation. And being so easily accessible it had also gained fame as the home of the Isthmian Games where boxers, wrestlers and runners competed fiercely against each other every two years, and where brave men fought wild animals to the death, almost on demand.

This leisure loving, pleasure loving commercial conflux, to which myriads of sailors brought goods from virtually every nation in the world to be sold by merchants and traders representing virtually every nation in the world, soon became a byword for all the vice of the world. If it was immoral or abnormal, warped or wicked, sick or sinful, it was common, and condoned, in Corinth.

And it was to that city I had come to present the light and life of the Gospel. As I walked in through its gates I committed myself humbly to God in fear and trembling, knowing that He and He alone could help me. If I hadn't learnt that before I most certainly should have learnt it from my most recent experiences in Athens, where my self-esteem had suffered a severe setback.

It was well on in the afternoon when I reached the heart of Corinth and I found it most interesting to stroll around, watching so many different people engaged in so many different pursuits. There were the usual shops for the wealthy Greek and Roman citizens in the colonnades around the agora, and then the less prestigious places, frequented by the poor, in the side streets.

As I walked idly down one of these side streets I was attracted by a strong smell I knew well. It was drifting out of an open-fronted shop and it was the unmistakeable odour of woven tent cloth.

Here was my opportunity!

If I was going to remain for any length of time in that city, I needed to work at something to help buy food and pay for somewhere to stay, and what better place to apply for a job than with a tentmaker! I could take up the trade in which I had been trained back in Tarsus, yet again!

Pushing past some tents displayed just inside the doorway, and obviously for sale, I saw a middle-aged man sitting on a small stool, stitching away, a half-sewn tent stretched out across his knees. He looked up as I walked in, and then presuming that I was a prospective customer he asked politely if he could help me.

"Yes, I hope you can," I began, in response to his enquiry. "I am a Jew from Tarsus in Cilicia and I as a boy I was taught the tentmaking trade. I have now come to Corinth, not as a tentmaker particularly, but as a messenger of the Gospel of Jesus Christ. However, I need a part-time job to help pay my expenses, and I was wondering if you would have any work that I could do?"

The tentmaker stood up and the colour drained from his face. He looked shocked, almost as though I had brought him some terrible news.

Curiously, though, that same face suddenly changed to split in a smile from ear to ear, as though I had brought him some tremendous news.

And then, to my complete surprise he dropped the tent he had been working at in a crumpled heap at his feet and disappeared through a curtain, out towards the back of the building!

"Priscilla! Priscilla! Come in here until you hear this!" I could hear him calling, presumably to someone outside, within seconds of leaving me.

I was really puzzled! What sort of a character was this tentmaker?

Thankfully I didn't have to wait long to find out, for almost as quickly as he had disappeared, he reappeared, with a pleasant looking woman hard on his heels.

Then, when they had offered me a spare stool on which to sit, I heard the most amazing story.

I had happened upon the home of Aquila and his wife Priscilla who were tentmakers by trade, but they were also Jews who had just less than a year before been expelled from Rome by a decree of Claudius Caesar. This edict had been issued because some 'fanatical' Jews had been causing unrest within the ranks of their own people throughout the empire and in the city by teaching about someone whom they called 'Chrestus'! Since the Romans had never even bothered to try and understand the ways of the Jewish nation, they thought it wise just to ban them from the capital to save this kind of unrest from becoming widespread.

It was how they explained it to me, though, that brought tears to my eyes.

"Since we are both Jews, but also both followers of Jesus Christ, called Christians," Priscilla said softly, "we thought it best, when forced to leave Rome, to come to Corinth where we knew there would be a market for our tents."

'Since we are both followers of Jesus Christ,' she had said.

I could hardly believe it!

And when they heard who I was, and how that God had called me to 'go far hence unto the Gentiles', Aquila and Priscilla offered me a job, and accommodation in a small spare room above the shop, straight away!

Within the space of a few hours in that notoriously corrupt city I had met people from my own nation, who earned their living at my chosen trade, and who shared the same God-given faith!

Suddenly at least some of my initial trepidation at coming to Corinth, and certainly all of my sense of loneliness, had disappeared. I was amongst friends. At last I had restored to me what I had most missed in the previous month or more, and that was the strength and solace that comes only in the company of like-minded believers.

The words of a Psalm of David, which I had learnt as a boy so many years before, came flooding back into my mind.

'I will instruct you and teach you in the way that you should go. I will counsel you and watch over you…. Many are the woes of the wicked, but the Lord's unfailing love surrounds the man who trusts in him.'

It was comforting to be assured of that once more.

And to prove it in practice.

What a joy it was in the weeks that followed, to settle into work with my new employers who were soon to become my close friends, and to share many things together. They were able to tell me about the few believers they knew in Rome, and I was able to tell them about the many believers I knew in nearly everywhere else!

Aquila and Priscilla were able to inform me, too, that there was a reasonably large Jewish settlement in Corinth, for the men of our nation were astute businessmen and where they saw a commercial opportunity they would attempt to make the best of it. And there were endless openings for entrepreneurs in cosmopolitan Corinth.

With such a concentration of Jews in one location there was bound to be a flourishing synagogue, and that is where Aquila, Priscilla and I went every Sabbath day.

It was good to lay aside the coarse cloth and the long needles of a tentmaker, for a day, and take up, read and teach the holy scriptures of truth. For many weeks I taught the large congregation of devout Jews and Greek God-fearers who met there, showing them that their Messiah had already come in the person of Jesus Christ, and that He had died for the sins not only of our nation, but also of the entire world, and that He had risen again from the dead.

The pious Jews, especially, had trouble accepting this message. A baby in a manger, a despised wandering preacher, or a crucified criminal, was not how they had ever imagined God's Anointed one, the conquering King of Kings, and Lord of Lords.

In a way there was nobody better suited than me to discuss such matters with them, for I had been where they were, once myself.

I could see that though many were actively opposed to my message, some were thinking, and asking very pertinent questions. But there were no immediate, or dramatic results. It would take time. I would just have to be patient.

Then one day, when I had been about a month in Corinth something happened which was set to give me another of those boosts, those heavenly tonics, that a tiring, teaching tentmaker so much needed.

Timothy and Silas arrived, unannounced, from Macedonia.

I was busily stitching away one morning, and busily chatting away to Aquila and Priscilla, who both happened to be there, when they suddenly appeared in the shop!

Their coming gave me a welcome lift in any number of ways.

The first of these was that they brought encouraging news from the churches in Macedonia. Timothy was able, and anxious to give me a very positive account of the growth and activities of the church in Thessalonica, and Silas filled me in on all the latest from Philippi.

And it was from the ever-generous saints in Philippi that I received a really comforting sense of succour and support. Not only were they advancing in the faith by leaps and bounds, but they had also sent me another substantial financial gift. This was to have a profound effect on my work because it meant that I didn't need to depend solely on making tents to make a living from then on, so I could concentrate more on my preaching and teaching.

The renewed fellowship of Timothy and Silas helped me in other, perhaps less obvious ways, too. Their very presence and their personal encouragement inspired me to teach much more fervently in the synagogue. And to write a letter.

As we discussed the state of the church back in Thessalonica I was overjoyed to learn that despite persecution the saints were going on joyfully with the Lord but I was also slightly worried to gather that some of them had become deeply concerned about some matters of doctrine.

When I was there I had been teaching them about the coming kingdom of our Lord, the Messiah. It appeared, however, that since then, some of the Christians' elderly relatives, who had also been believers, had died. Would they miss out on the joy of His second coming? anxious offspring wanted to know.

I sent Timothy along to a shop a few doors down to buy a scroll of papyrus and over the next few days I dictated a letter to them. As I tried to sit still with busy fingers, or as I strutted up and down with a buzzing brain, I prayed to God for wisdom, and then dictated a letter to 'my young son in the faith', as I loved to call him, who wrote it all down. My purpose was to encourage the saints who had already endured so much in the cause of Christ, and from whom the Gospel had sounded forth so freely, and to reassure them in relation to the coming of the Lord.

In a few days time the letter was complete, I read it over and signed it, and then Timothy and Silas set off again, back to Macedonia once more.

My more direct presentation of Christ, not only as the Promised One of the Jewish nation, but also as the Saviour of anyone who would trust in Him, be they Greek, Roman, Jew or anybody else, began to be more vehemently opposed in the synagogue. I knew it would be. For it usually always was.

When the leaders in the synagogues saw their control begin to slip and their congregations pay unusually rapt attention to the word of the Gospel, they invariably seemed to react aggressively.

And then one Sabbath morning, matters took a particularly ugly turn.

"Throw him out!" somebody called after I had begun to speak.

"We are not listening to any more of that stuff!" another strident voice took it up. "Expel him!"

Aware that we could soon have another all-out, full-scale, acrimonious confrontation on our hands, I loosened my robe and shook the skirt of it vigorously to signify that I was shaking off every speck of dust from the synagogue from about my being.

Then, looking straight at those who had been my most outspoken opposition, I announced, "Your blood be on your own head! I am clean! From now on I am going to preach to the Gentiles!"

Gasps of astonishment from some, and sighs of relief from others greeted this pronouncement, as I declined even to resume my seat, but strode out of that synagogue, never to be back.

God was in the move, however, for Justus, who was a Roman, but who had been one of the first to be saved in the city, offered me a room in his spacious house, right beside the synagogue, in which to hold regular meetings. This was tremendous, for many Corinthians, who were despised by the Jews, and whose lives were nothing more than a mixed up mess, flocked to hear what I had to say, and found peace and joy through trusting in Christ. These were people who would never, under any circumstances, have been permitted to enter the Jewish synagogue, but felt free to call at the house of Justus.

One of the most powerful demonstrations of God's power and presence with us in the proclamation of the Gospel in Corinth came just less than two weeks after my withdrawal from the synagogue.

I was in my room upstairs preparing to go out when I heard a man's voice addressing Aquila.

"Does Rabbi Paul live here?" the visitor was asking.

"Yes, he does," I could hear my host reply, rather cautiously.

"Could I speak to him a moment? I wish him no harm," the voice continued.

I was almost at the bottom of the stairs when I met Aquila on the way up. He looked perplexed.

"It is one of the rabbis from the synagogue, and he is asking for you, Paul," he whispered.

"Never worry, my friend, I will speak to him, " I replied, trying to calm his fears.

Aquila followed me into the workroom, where Priscilla was seated in a corner, anxiously awaiting developments.

As soon as I had entered the room a tall, dignified old man came across to me, and began to speak. I could judge by his demeanour that his earlier declaration had been correct. He meant me no harm.

"Sir, my opposition to you has been very public," he said softly but with unmistakeable sincerity, "so my confession will be before others as well. I have come to believe, after some serious study, that what you have been teaching us can only be true. Jesus of Nazareth is our Messiah, and I have therefore trusted in Him for my salvation."

Before he had finished the tears were trickling down my cheeks.

"That is wonderful news!" I told him spontaneously, and then we all held an impromptu Praise Service.

God had intervened in a marvellous way, once more!

The conversion of Crispus, and his defection from the synagogue to the house next door, however, brought increased antagonism from the Jews in the succeeding weeks. That, coupled with the fact that they often witnessed bigger crowds going into the house of Justus, than into the synagogue, irked them incredibly.

When some of our friends in the church told me of their murmuring and threatening, I became rather worried. Were they about to cause trouble for us? Was I about to be forced to flee from yet another city?

The prospect left me perturbed.

Then as I lay on my mat-bed one night the Lord appeared to me in a vision, and His comforting words quashed all my anxious concerns.

"Don't be afraid, Paul," came His reassurance. "Go on with your preaching and don't be silenced. Nobody's going to hurt you here. I have many people in this city."

I threw myself into the work with renewed vigour after that, and God continued to bless our endeavours for Him on a weekly, perhaps it could be said, even daily, basis.

Many Corinthians believed in the Lord Jesus, and I remained there both preaching the Gospel of the grace of God, and teaching the new believers.

And what a cross-section of the city these new believers were! We had Jews, Greeks and Romans, ranging from Erastus the city treasurer, and Crispus, the former chief rabbi in the synagogue, to any number of one-time thieves, swindlers, drunkards and prostitutes. These people all had the one thing in common. They were drawn together because they had each and every one confessed Christ as his or her own personal Saviour, and they both loved Him and owned Him as Lord of their lives.

Those were happy, blessed and spiritually productive days.

About a year and a half after I had first come to Corinth, though, things took another turn, for a new man sent from headquarters in Rome, called Gallio, replaced the existing Roman proconsul of the city.

This gave the seething, simmering Jews an idea. They hadn't been able to make any impression on the former governor with their complaints, but they thought that perhaps the newly appointed proconsul, who came with a reputation for gentle consideration, would be anxious to please all communities in his new charge. So they caught me teaching a group in the agora one day and dragged me before his judgement seat, the bema.

Gallio, seated on his high marble chair, had just begun hearing cases when the Jews hauled me up before him with the accusation, "Sir, this fellow is urging people to worship God in a manner contrary to the law."

I had stepped forward, and was about to speak up in my own defence when Gallio raised his hand.

Then he spoke. And I praised God for his wisdom.

"If you Jews were asking me to pass judgement on some serious crime," he said sternly, "then I would probably feel obliged to listen to you. But if you are here to talk about words and not deeds, about names and not things, about your law and not Roman law, sort it out amongst yourselves. I want nothing to do with it!"

As soon as he had finished that terse summing up he turned to his lictors and commanded, "Clear the court!" and this was an order they were more than happy to obey, as they jostled my Jewish accusers away.

And I was a free man once more!

The Lord, in my vision, had promised that nobody was going to hurt me there. And nobody did!

Unfortunately somebody did get hurt that day, though, for some of the Greeks, who were not passionately in love with their arrogant, as they saw them, Jewish fellow citizens, caught Sosthenes, Crispus' successor as chief of the synagogue, and one of my most vehement accusers, and gave him a thorough beating with their staves.

Even Gallio, the proconsul, turned a blind eye to this impromptu punishment. Perhaps he wasn't a big Jewish fan himself!

Gallio's ruling was an encouragement to me, however, for it implied that as long as I didn't contravene the Roman law, I could preach the Gospel wherever I liked, throughout the Empire.

The good news could make even further inroads, with further blessed results to the glory of God in the days and years to come. And soon after that incident I came to the considered conclusion that it was time to press forward with the message.

Priscilla and Aquila had decided to move to Ephesus to set up an overseas branch of their tent-making business in that Asian city with over a quarter of a million inhabitants, and I had a growing conviction that I should return to Jerusalem at Passover time and then travel on up to Antioch to report on a second very productive missionary journey. So we agreed, after much prayer, and some discussion, that we would leave Corinth together and they would accompany me as far as Ephesus and I would complete the remainder of the journey with Silas and Timothy.

There were some tearful partings in Corinth but when we had eventually managed to pull ourselves away we sailed across the southern Aegean from Cenchrea to the coast of Asia.

During my stopover in Ephesus I believe God showed me very definitely where my next fruitful mission field should be. On the two Sabbath days that I spent there, resting before taking the onward leg of my sea voyage to Caesarea, I took the opportunity of presenting Christ as God's Promised One, and our only Saviour, in the synagogue.

Perhaps it was because I had shaved my head in accordance with a vow I had taken, in Cenchrea, on my way there, or perhaps it was because the Ephesian Jews were more like their Berean, rather than their Thessalonian counterparts, but they seemed genuinely interested in the truth as I expounded it from the scriptures read amongst them.

"Please tell us more!" they begged.

I explained to them that I felt I should press on immediately towards Jerusalem and Antioch but that I would return to them as soon as possible.

It was quite amazing to hear people actually pleading to hear more about Jesus and His life and love, His death and resurrection, and His sacrifice for their sin!

I would be back, God willing!

Chapter Eighteen

BONFIRE NIGHT

By the grace of God, I was able to keep my promise.

The period between leaving Ephesus, with a burden to return, and actually getting back there had been a very busy six months. In that time I had gone to Jerusalem and passed on a gift for the poorer saints, revisited Antioch and reported on my previous journey, and then set off overland through Asia Minor. It was great to greet the friends in the churches in such places as Derbe and Iconium once more. And the joy and delight on the faces of Lois and Eunice when they saw their boy Timothy, who by then was a rapidly maturing young man, again, when we stopped off in Lystra, was a treat to treasure.

I was approaching Ephesus with only one change in my former team. Silas had remained behind in Jerusalem and Titus had joined Timothy and me for this latest trip.

Our paces quickened as we strode in through the swarming Smyrna gates in the four-mile wall surrounding Ephesus, and I was determined not to stop until I reached the recently set-up tent making concern of my close friends, Aquila and Priscilla.

The city we had just entered had been styled by many as 'the light of Asia' and I could sense that Titus, who had not been with us on our last brief visit there, was longing to slow down and soak up its splendour as I pressed ever forward. Ephesus was billed as the most magnificent of the magnificent cities of Asia, and it reminded me very much of Antioch in some respects with its wide, long colonnaded main thoroughfare paved in marble and its constantly buzzing streets and markets.

Rather than being the light of Asia however, Ephesus was more like the dark and wicked heart of Asia. The city was dominated by its most splendid ornament, the gleaming marble Temple of Diana, the goddess who had 'fallen down from heaven'. This temple, in all its architectural splendour, was reckoned to be one of the wonders of the world.

In addition to the worship of Diana, the goddess of wild nature and hunting, many of the citizen of Ephesus practised witchcraft and the occult. Hypnotism, black magic, crystal gazing, fortune telling and every conceivable cunning and curious art and device were common.

It would be some challenge to bring the light, life and love, which was only to be found through faith in Christ to these Gentiles!

How I coveted the company of those who loved my Saviour, and what a thrill it was to be with Aquila and Priscilla once more! They were so pleased to see us, and we had so much on which to bring each other up to date.

I wasn't long there until they found something for me to do, and as I eased myself back into the craft of cutting and stitching tent cloth, they told me their news from Ephesus, and asked me dozens of questions about the churches in Jerusalem, Antioch, Cilicia, and Galatia.

One of the most interesting, and most encouraging things they had to tell me was about a man called Apollos. This man had come to Ephesus and was teaching in the Jewish synagogue. Priscilla and Aquila sensed that he was a believer, who although an eloquent speaker, was lacking in some fundamental aspects of the knowledge of Christ and the gospel, so they undertook to give him a careful and considerate crash course in the Christian faith. It was with some pleasure that they told me that Apollos was now a most able and acceptable exponent of the holy scriptures and had just recently sailed across to Corinth to help the growing church over there.

Apollos had based his incomplete teaching on the message of repentance and baptism as proclaimed by John, and within two weeks of having arrived in Ephesus I met another group of twelve or so men who had also heard of John's baptism, but knew nothing of salvation by grace or the indwelling of the Holy Spirit. They were very eager to be taught and when I told them the story of Jesus they believed on Him and were baptized as Christians.

That provided a promising start to our stay in Ephesus, and for the first couple of months I was given a hearty welcome in the synagogue where I went to teach every Sabbath, too. My promised return to the city had been eagerly anticipated and for a while my teaching, if not generally accepted, was at least generously tolerated.

However, as I began to explain the way of salvation, and the forgiveness of sins for all, through the death of our Lord Jesus Christ on Calvary, some were not so well pleased.

It was the old old story. The two big problems raised their heads again. One concerned the Jews' age-long perception of the Messiah, and the other their passionate desire to preserve the purity of their religion.

"How could a poor wandering preacher with only a mere handful of untaught disciples and who was callously crucified as a criminal, be God's Promised Saviour of our proud though oppressed nation?" they demanded defiantly one day.

Then a few weeks later I was faced with the other common objection to my preaching.

"Are you trying to tell us that we are to mix with the Gentiles, and eat with them, and treat them as if they were Jews?" they enquired indignantly. "We are quite happy for them to learn and keep the laws of the faith of our fathers, and then progress from that into your Christian church if they must. But otherwise we will have nothing to do with them, or indeed for that matter, with you!"

This hardening of attitude helped me recognize that it was time to take my message out of the synagogue and into the streets of yet another teeming heathen city.

There were so many people in Ephesus with enslaved souls and blinded minds who needed to hear the emancipating and enlightening news of freedom from sin, and positive peace through trusting in Christ, that I considered it unwise to preach to those who didn't want to hear any longer.

I decided not to return to the synagogue and after making a few enquiries came to an agreement with a teacher called Tyrannus who owned a lecture hall in the heart of the city.

Tyrannus held his lectures from seven until eleven every morning and then again in the late afternoon from four o'clock onwards. When I approached him he proved quite agreeable to rent out the hall to me in the siesta hours when he wasn't using it, from eleven until four.

This worked well for two very practical reasons.

I could work for Aquila and Priscilla in the early morning and late evening work periods and teach the word and truth of God to all who were interested during my out-of-work midday hours. It followed also that since it was the heat of the day rest period and I was off work, then virtually everybody else would be off work too! And if they were not at work they would be free to come along to the lecture hall to hear me speak.

And many did.

God helped us in those days and we were privileged to see many from all ranks and classes in the city led to faith in Him. But if God blessed our work, Satan certainly opposed it. There were times when we felt squeezed and pressed from two entirely different directions.

On one side we had the Jews for whom our 'liberal' teaching of peace and love to all, whoever they happened to be, through simple faith in Christ, didn't go far enough, and on the other side we had all the wizards and astrologers of Ephesus for whom that same message went much too far.

Neither of these factions was disposed to make life easy for us, and they didn't. There were many struggles, much either openly expressed or subtly executed opposition, and many tears.

Souls were saved in spite of the hostility, however, not only in the city but also in the outlying areas, for although I wasn't often free to accompany them because of my job in tent making and my teaching in the school of Tyrannus, Timothy, Titus, Gaius and Aristarchus preached in a number of the larger towns and cities around. Many came to faith in Christ in these places and embryo churches were born and began to move on into infancy.

As news of blessing in these districts helped lift my spirits, so disturbing news from Corinth helped dash them and smash them again.

Disquieting rumours had begun to filter through to Ephesus about the state of the church in that city, a church which had been so happy, and so united, when I had left. That though, I began to realize, for time had seemed to pass so quickly, had been almost three years before.

The new believers had been left to live out their lives in very wicked surroundings, where Christian purity and honesty were the butt of many a joke, and where everything tended to drag them back into the old evil life. Corinth was not heaven, Christ had not come back, and resisting the Evil One had not been easy, I understood all that. But moral standards had begun to slip, I discovered, and that worried me.

Then, as if to confirm my worst fears, some Christians from the household of Chloe arrived in Ephesus and were able to give me a first hand account of the current situation in Corinth. And I wished I didn't have to hear it!

It came as a real body blow to me for it was more than disturbing what they told me. It was downright distressing.

A party spirit had arisen within the church, apparently, and they had formed into four splinter groups, each of which claimed to be the devotees of a different leader. Some were Apollos' followers, some were Peter's, some were Christ's, and worst of all, some were mine!

My informants were fit to tell me, too, that a number of the brethren had been drinking excessively in some of the church gatherings, to the extent of having become drunk on occasions, and that open immorality was being practised, uncondemned.

I was horrified.

Something would have to be done at once to counter such error. And the most effective way, I reckoned, of addressing this very serious situation, was to write them a letter.

So, after a period of much prayer and deep communion with God, I dictated a letter to Timothy and Sosthenes, in which I endeavoured to sort out the problems of the church, whilst encouraging them as best I could as well.

It was both painful and painstaking work, for I had to express myself in such a way as to correct the obvious deviations within the church community in Corinth without ostracizing the offending believers, for whom life in that totally godless city was already difficult enough. The writing of letters to the various churches, was something I had felt led to undertake, however, as inspired by God, as a natural extension of my widening ministry. For by then I felt not only responsible for pioneering with the Gospel into difficult situations like the one in which I currently found myself in Ephesus, but also for the constant shepherding care of the churches which were already up and running. There was no way that I could desert them to their own devices and the Devil's trickery.

But God supplied me with all the strength, wisdom and grace for the task, as He had ever and always done. It was amazing too, how that He granted special power in a special situation.

Ephesus was a city steeped in the occult. So therefore men judged the authority and legitimacy of a teacher or leader in that society, not so much by what he said as by what he did. Not so much by his ability to propound mysterious doctrines as by his capacity to perform mysterious deeds.

And in that environment, and specifically for that environment, God worked special miracles through me, as a sign to the magic-mad citizens of Ephesus. Not long after I had arrived in the city and had returned to the tent making trade, it was discovered by some that if they took the sweat rags and aprons, which I had worn at my work, and laid them on the sick they were healed, and evil spirits were exorcised from the demon-possessed.

This served to highlight God's power in my work, and as a result many came to my daily teaching sessions and were saved.

When a group of itinerant Jewish exorcists heard of this success of our ministry in Ephesus they decided to try and use the name of

Jesus as part of their evil incantations. It didn't work, however, for the man who was possessed of the evil spirit they were attempting to cast out turned and set upon them, yelling, "Jesus I recognize, and Paul I know, but who are *you*?"

So fierce was this frenzied attack that the crowd of charlatans were thankful to escape with their lives!

When news of this event spread like wildfire around the city it had a profound effect on both the deeply religious Jews, and the wholly irreligious Greeks, living there.

It struck terror into the hearts of the Jews for they had often heard read or recited in the synagogue, 'You shall not take the name of the Lord your God in vain,' and it also commanded the immediate attention and respect of the superstitious, but as yet unbelieving, Greeks.

In both cases, and in both communities, the name of the Lord Jesus, which had been taken in vain with such dramatic consequences, began to be honoured and reverenced.

There was another extremely significant outcome of the failed exorcism attempt, and the widely reported attack on the bogus exorcists, in that it created a crisis point in the lives of many new Christians. Quite a number of them had, as I had suspected, been finding it a tremendous struggle to deliver themselves, by the help of God's Holy Spirit, from the mystical ties which had once held them bound to the dark world of witchcraft and evil spirits.

On hearing of the routing of the wandering hoaxers, however, they determined to make a clean break with the past.

As the darkness of night settled over that city battling to free itself from the darkness of sin, one evening, a crowd of recent believers followed me to the main square of the city. That afternoon, in the lecture hall of Tyrannus I had been speaking out, as I had done so often, about the enveloping wickedness in our world, and citing the example of the repulse of the sly sons of Sceva, as an illustration of the power of the Lord to prevail over all evil.

The Christians had become convinced that the time had come to make a public declaration that they had made a clean break with the past, confessing what they felt, that they had become completely new people through faith in Christ.

These men and women had searched their homes for every sign or symbol of their former lifestyles and loaded with books of spells and mystic formulas, charms and amulets were on their way to rid themselves of them, forever.

And what a bonfire we had that night! When all these courageous new Christians had piled up their books and instruments of magic, they invited me to set them alight with a torch someone handed me.

In the space of half an hour all the tools of the trade of many former evil artisans went up in smoke. And the amazing thing was, too, that when others, who had not been believers up until then, saw the bold witness of their erstwhile associates they also surrendered their books to the blaze!

The heat of the fire became so intense at one time that the curious crowd, which had gathered to see what was going on, was forced to fall back. And in the light of the fire strange things showed up. Here an incantation in a foreign language, would curl up, crumple and disappear, or over there a gaily coloured picture would suddenly blacken and somewhere else it would be a drawing of circles within circles or a recipe for a potent poison.

In that single thirty-minute period on that big bonfire night many lifetime collections of the magician's craft, worth vast sums of money, were reduced to a grey ash which floated, settled, and smelt, all over the city.

The word of the Lord had made impressive inroads into Ephesus!

The bonfire in the square had set everybody thinking, and had consequently resulted in a serious slump in the sales of the small statues of Diana, the famous goddess of the city, which were either sculpted in wood or marble, or moulded in silver or porcelain, by the local craftsmen.

This drop in sales became so serious that it spurred Demetrius, the President of the Guild of Silversmiths that year, to incite opposition to our position and preaching.

He pretended to be terribly worried that the image of their great Diana would be despised, but his main concern was that if the current trend continued, he would, with many others, be forced out of business.

When he had delivered a passionate speech designed to fire the local craftsmen all up to fever pitch, a mob descended on the Jewish quarter and Aquila's tent making shop.

They were after me, and I hate to imagine what would have happened if I had been at home. But I wasn't. When my employers, who also doubled as my host and hostess and close Christian friends, heard the mob chanting in the streets, 'Great is Diana of the Ephesians!' they knew that I was in danger, and risking their own safety, told me to hide.

On failing to find me, the incensed idol-makers and the riotous rabble they had succeeded in collecting around them, captured Gaius and Aristarchus, two of my team, and dragged them up through the streets to the city's massive amphitheatre, chanting all the way. On hearing of the capture of my companions I wanted to rush up there to defend them but both the local Christians and some of my influential friends on the city council advised against it. Having experienced the mood of a mob of fanatical Ephesians on previous occasions they informed me quite pointedly that such an intervention. could do more harm than good.

So all that was left for me to do was pray, committing the matter into the capable Hands of my Heavenly Father. And that is what I did.

Over many years in His service I had found that God often answered my prayers by performing an extraordinary miracle by purely ordinary means, and He did it on this occasion.

Two hours of shouting does a good deal to tire people, particularly if they don't know what it is they are shouting about in the first place, and the whole mad uproar that afternoon all fizzled out after a very wise speech by the town clerk.

If Diana was as great as they all believed she was, he told them, then she could look after herself, and as for us, since we had neither committed sacrilege nor blasphemed their goddess, there was no case to answer!

Immediately after that speech Gaius and Aristarchus were allowed to go free, and in the eyes of the citizens of another heathen city our preaching had been totally vindicated and the witness and testimony of the newly-formed church there advanced.

Our God had come to our aid, in the furtherance of His work, another time.

And with such a clear sky behind me, but with tempers raised around me, I soon began to feel that it was time to move on again.

There were some men I longed to see, and matters I needed to sort out, in Macedonia, once more.

Chapter Nineteen

ESCAPING DEATH, BUT NOT SCARED TO DIE

It soon became evident that my life was now in danger in Ephesus, and I had to quit the city sooner rather than later, that was for sure.

Since I wanted to visit as many of the Macedonian churches as possible, for practical as well as personal reasons, I decided to set off northwards. While still in Ephesus I had organised a collection in all the Gentile churches for the believers in Jerusalem who were finding it difficult to obtain food in another famine in Palestine. I wanted therefore to finalize the fundraising effort and convey the proceeds to those in need as soon as ever possible. And on a personal level I very much longed to renew fellowship with so many who were very dear to me and for whom I thanked the Lord continually.

Having made a hurried withdrawal from Ephesus I travelled northwards as far as Troas, intending to wait there for Titus, whom I assumed would pass through that port on his return from Corinth. I had become most impatient to hear how the Corinthians had received my earlier letter, and my trusted messenger, Titus, would have that vital information.

I waited for weeks, though, and he didn't appear. My spirit grew restless and I became increasingly depressed. During that stay in Troas I battled through a cloud of gloom to preach the Gospel at every opportunity, and souls were saved and added to the small, but growing, church.

It was difficult to settle.

Where was Titus? I wondered. What was keeping him in Corinth? Had things turned really nasty, and he had decided not to come back?

All kinds of crazy thoughts crossed my mind, but all I could do was put my trust in God and keep going.

When my anxious agitation became unbearable I decided to travel on to Philippi. Perhaps Titus would come that way, and even if he didn't I would have Luke, Lydia and lots of others to help remind me of what God had already done in that city. Timothy, my constant companion, was with me on that trip, across to Neapolis and on to Philippi, just as he had been when I had first travelled there, but we had two new additions to our party as well. During our three years or so in Ephesus, two promising young men called Tychicus and Trophimus had come to faith in Christ, and sensing that they had potential for God I entrusted them with transporting the Ephesus gift to Jerusalem.

We had only been a matter of days in Philippi when Titus turned up there. I was overjoyed to see him, and generally pleased to hear his report. It appeared from his account that most of the Corinthians had received my letter graciously, and had taken it to heart. Steps had been taken to amend many of the matters crying out for urgent attention in the church. That could only be good, and for that I genuinely praised God.

Unfortunately, however, although Titus was able to paint a much brighter picture, it was not a picture with a warm and comforting sun blazing out of a completely cloudless sky.

There were some, it seemed, who had even questioned my authority to send out such a letter.

"Who does Paul think he is?" they had been enquiring scathingly. "Sure he is not even a real apostle. We devout Jews are more genuine than he is, for in truth he is nothing more than a Pharisee who has forsaken the true faith. And just take a look at him! He is trying to sound like some God-given teacher, but he certainly doesn't *look* like one!"

After giving myself a day or two to totally debrief Titus, and pray to God for grace and guidance, I decided to write to the Corinthians again. I felt it imperative that I should express my delight at the obedience of some, and my disgust at the cutting comments of others.

And just to add to my burden, when I was at Philippi, struggling to write that letter, I fell sick again. I had another bout of malaria, which always seemed to come back when my physical strength and spiritual stamina were at their lowest ebb. Although the sickness was most debilitating I was happy at least, if I had to fall ill, to have fallen ill in Philippi where I had been able to renew my association with Doctor Luke who was able to help me in a couple of ways. He cared for my bodily condition as well as helping Timothy and Titus, from time to time, with the actual writing of the letter as I dictated it.

When Titus had set off by sea with my reply to Corinth, and I had recovered sufficiently to travel on, I set out westward across the Via Egnatia, surrounded by a mountain of memories and again accompanied by the three T's, Timothy, Tychicus and Trophimus. We revisited Thessalonica and Berea and when we had heard all their news, told them all ours, and tried to strengthen them in the Lord, we followed my letter of about two months before and arrived in Corinth in early winter.

Those who had been so vociferous when opposing me at a distance, proved not to be so brave when it came to facing me in person, and we were pleased to be compelled, both by seasonal conditions and my heartfelt desire, to stay there for the remainder of the winter. Since all sailings across the Great Sea had been suspended until the spring I decided to use that time quietly consolidating the church in Corinth.

Nevertheless, it is wonderful how God works.

For during that winter stopover I felt guided by Him to undertake a project which I had not ever really contemplated before. It so happened that for years, and especially since becoming so close to Aquila and Priscilla and hearing their descriptions of the hub of the

Empire, I had become possessed with an ever-increasing aspiration to see Rome.

Never having had a chance to turn that dream into reality, I had put it to the back of my mind until Phoebe came across from Cenchrea, where she lived, to see me one day.

This Phoebe was a wealthy widow, and a fine Christian, in whose home Silas, Priscilla, Aquila and I had stayed for a few nights on a previous trip through the port of Corinth. There was so much to talk about, but in the course of conversation I gathered that she was soon about to set out for Rome on business.

This gave me an idea.

I would write to the Christians in the Imperial Capital and Phoebe could act as courier. The writing of such a letter would afford me the opportunity of making an initial contact with them, and informing them of my intention to visit them at a later date, possibly even as part of a longer trip to Spain.

More importantly, though, it would allow me to make a complete written statement of the basic arguments outlining how that justification by faith in Christ had superseded justification by the works of the law. It was essential that everyone should be clear that Christ's death on Calvary had provided salvation for all, not just for the Jew alone, and that this salvation could only be procured through personal faith in Him.

The problem of Jewish non-acceptance of Gentile believers had dogged the early churches for years. I had already addressed it at white heat in a letter to the Galatians. Now, having had further opportunity to reflect, it was possibly time to expound the matter at greater length and in greater depth, as God saw fit to guide.

For days and nights we worked at it. Since my stay in Corinth on this occasion would of necessity be of short duration I did not undertake any manual work, but rather occupied my time counselling those who came to see me, and in writing.

A young amanuensis called Tertius came almost daily to my lodgings in the house of Gaius, and I dictated a letter to the Romans to the sound of this reed-pen scratching its way across the papyrus. When at last it was finished, and I read it over before signing, I felt satisfied. It was, when complete, what I had intended it to be, a manifesto of the Christian faith. This, I prayed would be read to the blessing of believers, not only in Rome, but also in many other locations besides.

At last the long winter was over.

Flower buds had begun to open, the swallows had returned from Egypt, the sailing schedule had resumed on the Great Sea, Phoebe had just left for Rome, and all those who had been coordinating the collection for the Jerusalem church had assembled in Corinth. It was now time to embark upon the final phase of the project, that of transporting all the lovingly donated gifts to where they would be most needed, and hopefully most gratefully received.

Soon after Timothy and Aristarchus had begun to make enquiries about a crossing to Syria, from where we could easily travel overland to Jerusalem, we became aware of a potentially serious problem.

Late one night, under cover of darkness, a local believer who had just come up from Cenchrea, gave us some startling news.

My travel agents had been trying to arrange a passage on a pilgrim-ship taking both Greek and Asian Jews to the Passover in Jerusalem. Prices on such a specially charted vessel would be more reasonable than on a normal trading ship, but the company, we gathered, would be less congenial.

The rumour was that a number of the fanatical Corinthian Jews who had never quite been able to forget their humiliation before Gaius, and who regarded me as a total heretic anyway, had heard that my name would possibly be on the passenger list of one of the ships taking the express route to Jerusalem, and had hatched a plan to have me assassinated.

A substantial bribe to a hard-up and crooked captain, the flash of a dagger in the moonlight, a stab in the heart, and the soft splash of a body being slipped silently overboard into the sea, could see me end my days prematurely.

In the light of such information, plans had to be changed at short notice.

We agreed to begin our journey as soon as possible, but not all together, and not all by boat.

Having arranged to rendezvous with the main body of our Jerusalem-bound party in Troas, I set out overland with the remainder.

It would be slightly less worrying to run the risk of a bandit attack on the land than an assassination attempt at sea, I reckoned!

After slightly more than a week's walking we arrived in Philippi and remained there over the Passover period, since we hadn't been able to make it to Jerusalem by feast time, as I had intended. Then I was glad to have Luke back in the company, as bearer of the Philippian contribution to the Jerusalem collection, when we pressed on yet again. The winds were against us on our short voyage south from Neapolis, and the journey, which should have taken two days, took five, but when we eventually arrived in Troas harbour it was to find a mightily relieved group awaiting us.

We had a week to wait in Troas for the next suitable boat, so I spent hours talking to my old friends Timothy, Titus and Luke, and encouraging the local believers as often as possible.

Our last night there was on the first day of another week, and on that night the church had met together, after work, to hold their breaking of bread service. This meeting had been convened in a large room, three stories up, and approached by an outside staircase. One of the more well off members owned the house and he had allowed the church group to use his large upstairs room for that particular gathering. Since I was the expected speaker, a larger than normal crowd was expected, apparently! That, coupled with the fact that there were no less than nine other men in my travel party, made the more spacious accommodation very welcome.

Soon after sunset the crowds began to gather, and before it was time for the service to commence the place was packed. They were pushed and crushed in everywhere, and it was still really hot. The air hung heavy with a clammy, stifling heat.

After we had taken the bread and wine of the communion service I began to exhort the believers at great length. There was so much about the grace and love of God, and about practical Christian living in their situation that I felt they needed to know, that I didn't notice the time passing. I just felt inspired to go on and on.

As it wore on towards midnight the grey-black oily smoke from the many spluttering lamps, and the already oppressive heat of that particular night, left some of my congregation looking decidedly drowsy.

There was one lad in particular, I had noticed. He was about thirteen or fourteen years of age I reckoned, and in the earlier part of the meeting he had been staring intently at me with a sort of hero worship in his eye, and had been listening to all I said.

Latterly though, he had jammed himself in an open window aperture, probably to make the best of any breath of fresh air that sultry night could offer from any quarter. And as I spoke I could see him slumping further and further down. He had obviously fallen asleep.

Suddenly there was the sound of a piercing cry, followed almost immediately by a sickening thud.

The lad was out the window! From three storeys up!

I lost my congregation at once.

Everybody rushed for the outside staircase and tumbled down it in shocked confusion. When I could reach it through the crush, I descended too, and by the time I reached the motionless form, still and white in the dim starlight, Doctor Luke was bending over it, shaking his head.

"He's not breathing, and there's no heartbeat, Paul. He's dead," he whispered.

A mother's wail rent the night air.

"Don't worry, his life is still in him," I assured them, in apparent contradiction to my learned and respected medical friend. I felt, however, that God could work another miracle in this situation, and so I threw myself down and held the body close to the warmth of my own body until I felt it breathing again.

Eutychus, as I was soon to be told the lad was called, had been restored to life, much to the joy of his parents and friends and also to the glory of God.

What a night we had after that! We drifted back upstairs, held a prayer and praise service, shared a communal meal and talked on and on until the morning. And even at that, morning seemed to come too soon!

For in the morning we had to leave, some of us by boat and others walking overland part of the way. Not having made Jerusalem for Passover, I was determined to be there for Pentecost if at all possible, and that only allowed us fifty days to make quite a long journey. So we had to keep pushing on.

When we arrived at the port of Miletus, though, after some four days at sea, we were told that we would have a long weekend to spend in the harbour there while cargoes were exchanged. Since I had no intention of wasting time aboard a ship heaving with porters and merchants, I realized that there was a way in which I could spend the time profitably for God, by supporting and strengthening the leaders of a steadily growing church.

Miletus was just thirty-five miles south of Ephesus on a good road, so I dispatched Timothy and Aristarchus, who had both been present during my bonfire night and afternoon riot experiences in the City of Diana, on a mission. These two men had already travelled extensively around the city during their previous three year stay there, so they knew all the roads, but they also knew all the leaders of the church personally. And their task was to find these elders and invite them to come and see me at Miletus as soon as possible.

In just over two days time the party returned. The elders from the church at Ephesus appeared genuinely glad to see me again and told me all their latest news.

When I had heard their full report I addressed them on the rocky beach. Since our 'headquarters' in the port of Miletus was a trading ship swarming with slaves in the harbour, my only option was to speak to these earnest, caring men, outdoors.

So to the background music of waves lapping on the shore and the shouts of seamen and traders from the harbour I opened my heart to them as they sat around me on big stones and small rocks.

My point of contact was to dip back into the past, reminding them of the joys and problems of my former visit to Ephesus. I reminded them of the days and nights of teaching and of tears, of the opposition by the Jews, and of my work as a tentmaker to help make ends meet.

There were nods and smiles of recognition as I recalled some of the experiences we had shared as God had worked mightily in the formation of a testimony for Him in their city.

Since hearing of the assassination plot being hatched in Corinth, however, I had been possessed with a strange sense of foreboding about the trip I was at that time taking to Jerusalem. The elders knew of the purpose of my trip as they had helped coordinate the collection, which was by then in the charge of Trophimus and Tychicus, but they seemed concerned when I told them of my fears for the future.

My purpose in bringing them together, though, had not been to talk about myself, and when I had expressed my personal feelings I then counselled them as to their further service for God. I felt compelled to give them three basic bits of advice. They should be careful not to be tempted into sin, they should take constant care of the flock of God, and they should be ever alert against false teachers who could cause untold havoc amongst them. And as our time together came to an end I summarised for them the teachings of the Master Himself in the words, 'it is more blessed to give than to receive'.

When some of my travelling companions came along to where we were huddled on the beach and announced softly that our ship had been ordered to hoist sail, and that we were to return to it immediately for embarkation, I was touched by the reaction of those we were leaving behind on the shore.

Towards the end of my message to them, prompted perhaps by my increasing apprehension, I had told them that I would probably never see them again this side of heaven. That was almost too much for most of them.

After we had knelt down and prayed together on the shore I could hardly drag myself away towards the ship. My travelling companions were striding on ahead of me, anxious not to miss the boat, yet still the Ephesian elders clung around my neck. It was most moving to see grown men so touched. But I had to leave.

So it was with a heavy heart that I had to almost tear myself out of their embraces and step across on to the deck, ready to set sail.

Those men seemed to stand on the quay at Miletus until our ship disappeared from their view. Then presumably they would return to Ephesus to try to put into practice all that God had guided me to tell them.

We had a long trip lasting over a week across the eastern end of the Great Sea after that, calling in at a few harbours on the way until we finally reached the port of Tyre on the west coast of Palestine.

Since it would take some time to unload all the wine, grain and purple cloth that we had been carrying I again made an effort to contact the small group of believers in that coastal city. As with others we had visited, they seemed only too happy to see us, but some of the men there, who had a number of contacts in Jerusalem, and who reckoned they could gauge the still angry mood of my former colleagues, the Jewish leaders, advised against continuing as far as the capital.

Despite my own secret personal premonitions, and their earnest admonitions, I was determined to proceed, nonetheless. I had a job to do, and a gift to deliver, so I would finish the job by supervising the delivery of the gift. That, I was convinced, was God's will for me, but I suppose there was an element of personal pride in it, too. I could never tolerate spineless shirkers, and since I had put my 'hand to the plough', I would *not* be turning back!

We had a week in Tyre before we were ready to sail on again to Caesarea, and before we left, on our last afternoon there, we had another beach prayer meeting. This time though it was not only men who attended. The local Christians had turned out in force! I could see all the passing sailors, slaves and local layabouts gazing curiously at us as a whole group of men, women and children knelt down on the beach while some of the local elders prayed for God's blessing on our continued journey.

After another tearful parting we sailed southwards to Caesarea, which was to be our final destination before striking inland for Jerusalem.

And it was at Caesarea that I received my final warning.

We were stopping over in the home of Philip the evangelist when Agabus the prophet, whom I had met years earlier in Antioch, arrived down from Jerusalem. Whether he had called in response to a God-given direction, or whether Philip's four daughters, who themselves had expressed misgivings about my plans, had sent for him, I have never been quite sure.

In any event, he used his own unique and often dramatic style of presentation to get what he claimed to be God's message across to me. With one swift movement he unfastened the girdle around my cloak and tied himself up with it, binding first his feet and then his hands, as tightly as he could.

"The Holy Spirit has revealed to me that this is what the Jews of Jerusalem will do to the owner of this girdle, before turning him over to the Gentiles for judgement!" he announced solemnly.

Everyone stood aghast.

The prophecies of Agabus had always come true in the past, they knew.

What will Paul do now? they wondered.

Passionately, individually, and in genuinely grieving groups, they begged me not to go on to Jerusalem.

Timothy and Luke, who knew me so well and loved me so much, having been through so much with me, just stood crying, pleading long and hard.

But I was determined.

"What do you mean by standing there crying?" I asked them, for their tender tears had touched me. "If I am breaking your heart, you are certainly breaking mine as well. Do you not understand that I am not afraid to be bound, and I'm not even scared to die if it comes to that, for the name of the Lord Jesus?"

They seemed to sense that I was not for turning, and left off after that.

"The will of the Lord be done," they conceded, more grudgingly than graciously.

I was glad they had reached that decision at last, after all the wearisome warnings and weeping.

For I had always known it would be.

Chapter Twenty

AWAY WITH HIM!

It was a pleasure to be back in Jerusalem after that final two-day trip from Caesarea. I had been to the Holy City at different times, and for different reasons before, and this particular visit should be set to give me the greatest thrill of them all.

In years gone past I had been there as a student, as a new Christian after my experience on the road outside Damascus, and a couple of times with my old friend Barnabas, both conveying a gift and contending for the faith.

This latest trip was to donate an alms, a substantial, and in many cases sacrificial, gift, which had been systematically collected amongst the Gentile Christians, for the needy believers in Jerusalem. Surely if anything should be gratefully received and prove practically, more than any preaching ever could, that we were all one in Christ Jesus, regardless of who we were or where we came from, that should.

It would be wonderful if it was, but I still had my sneaking fears.

My friends had told me that no matter what happened the will of God would be done, and I was happy to agree with them. It wasn't God I had the problem with, though. He had never let me down before and wouldn't then, I knew. It was men I was worried about. They had proved so fickle in the past. How would *they* react now?

If even the slightest vestige of the animosity I had encountered amongst the men of my nation in Antioch in Pisidia, or Thessalonica, or just recently when preparing to leave Corinth, still remained in Jerusalem, then we could have problems.

Our first night in the city was great. We moved around greeting individual believers whom I knew, and as I introduced all the men in my party to them everyone seemed genuinely glad to see us. It augured well for the future. Perhaps I had been worrying about nothing!

The next morning proved to be the big test, though, for that was when it was arranged that we should meet James and the other elders of the Jerusalem church.

The early part of the encounter went well.

The assembled elders invited me to tell them about my work for God and I was glad of the opportunity to do so.

It was mildly amusing to watch the expressions of some of those earnest, elderly gentlemen who sat, leaning forward, chin cupped in hand, gazing at me with undivided attention as I spoke. I could only assume that some of them had never been on a ship or left their own Judean hills in their lives. And I could be quite sure that they had never been caught up in a riot or forced to sidestep an assassination attempt! Yet they nodded knowledgeably as I told them enthusiastically, for I was bubbling over with it since it had been my life's work, of songs in prison, about storms at sea, and about souls saved in Galatia, Asia, Macedonia, and the remainder of Greece.

Then when I had finished my account of God's marvellous dealings amongst the Gentiles I called forward my friends from many of the places I had just mentioned, to present the monetary gifts with which they had been entrusted.

Timothy and Gaius were the first pair to step forward with the gift from the churches in Galatia.

Then came Aristarchus and Secundus from Thessalonica, Sopater from Berea, and Luke from Philippi, bearing separate contributions from the Macedonian believers.

When they had sat down again Titus came over from one side and laid a bag from Corinth at the feet of the elders.

And finally, Tychicus and Trophimus, two more recent Christians from Ephesus came up rather nervously and presented the offering from the churches in their part of Asia.

When collected together into one place all the gifts made quite an impressive pile. And, if wisely distributed, all that money would doubtless bring relief to hundreds of God's famine-oppressed people in the capital.

For a few moments the elders appeared deeply impressed and genuinely grateful. They seemed awestruck almost.

"Praise God!" they exclaimed, spontaneously. "Glory to God for all these wonderful works which He has done through His servant Paul!"

The air was filled with praise, and their hearts were filled with thankful thoughts for unknown but unselfish fellow-believers in faraway places.

Those were magic moments.

But unfortunately, they were only moments.

It was amazing to watch how the countenances of those elders slowly changed.

Gradually the glow of the wider vision faded, and the restricting bonds of the Jews in Jerusalem tightened around them once more, wiping all the fervour from their faces and the passion from their voices.

The first man to speak changed the mood of the meeting completely.

"Brother, you must be careful," he said solemnly, lowering his voice. "Our people here are very concerned about your ministry. They believe that you are disregarding the Law of Moses and that you are going about teaching that there is no difference between uncircumcised Gentiles and God's chosen people. They will soon find out that you are in the city and they could make things awkward for you."

I was taken aback by this but didn't have time to respond to it before another took it up.

"We have a plan to clear you of all suspicion," he went on, half whispering and half smiling as though he was about to bestow some fantastic favour upon me. "Listen. We have four men here who have taken a Jewish vow. You could be their sponsor and go to the Temple with them daily, paying their charges for shaving their heads and the other purification ceremonies. If you did this all men would be convinced that you were a loyal Jew and there would be no problem."

There was a stupefied silence when he had finished and I looked around at the faithful friends, who had been through so much with me, and were sitting or standing about. Timothy was the only one of the whole lot of them who had any Jewish blood in his veins, and he, with the rest, looked totally bewildered. I think they felt sorry for me.

It was, for them, most of whom had trusted in Christ and turned to God from idolatry, rather hard to understand.

As a group we had set at their feet thousands of pieces of silver in a collection, which had taken more that two years of thought and planning to correlate. We had risked our lives and travelled hundreds of miles under sometimes very difficult conditions to bring it to them.

I had just given them a vivid account of all my work for the Lord, of all the heathen who had been saved, and of all the churches that had been founded in the west.

And here they were outlining some scheme they had devised to save me from being an embarrassment to them in Jerusalem!

It was time for leadership. No matter how sick I felt inside I would have to demonstrate meekness, strength under control, before my loyal friends who were perhaps feeling a little let down.

I understood the problem facing the Jewish elders and their counsel was no doubt wise and well intended given the volatile situation in Jerusalem.

So I went along with it. I had no problems with the Nazarite vows of my people and if it kept the peace for my brethren in Jerusalem, I was quite happy to fall in with their plan.

What the church elders hadn't considered, however, was that although their plan might go some way to placating the fervent Judaists within the local church, it also brought me into undesirable prominence amongst the fanatical Jews from every country of the Empire, who were daily crowding the temple courts.

About the third day of my seven day commitment to the four men with the vow, I was walking through the streets talking enthusiastically to Trophimus, and pointing out some of the main buildings to him, when we met a group of Asian Jews who kept staring at us.

"That was Alexander the coppersmith, a Jew from Ephesus, we just met there," Trophimus remarked casually as we walked on. "Remember him? He was the one who got caught up in the riot in the city the day they would probably have killed you if they had caught you!"

Three days later, I was to meet that man Alexander again, with some of the other Asian Jews, in a much more menacing confrontation.

I had just entered the inner court of the temple on my way through to meet with the four men with the vow, that day, when I heard a frenzied cry.

"To the rescue, men of Israel!" the coppersmith from Ephesus screamed, having spotted me at a distance. He then came rushing at me, his finger pointed in accusation. Directly behind him I could see four or five of his fired-up friends, their eyes flashing fury. "This is the fellow who has been teaching everybody everywhere against the Chosen People, the Law of Moses and this Holy Temple!"

The rallying cry rang out across the crowded temple court and suddenly I became conscious that angry men were converging upon me from all sides.

Pleased with the response to the initial call, one of Alexander's Asian companions carried the accusations a step further. "And to make matters worse," he yelled, "he has brought Greeks into the Temple and has polluted this Holy Place!"

That allegation was patently untrue. I had done no such thing, but since they had seen me in the city with Trophimus a few days before they blamed me for taking him into the temple.

Within seconds I was being punched and pummelled from all sides.

"Away with him! Kill him! Away with him!" the mob began to chant.

I was then dragged, pushed, pulled and kicked across to the Beautiful Gate and tossed violently down the fifteen steps to the outer court, The Court of the Gentiles.

As I tumbled down the steps, trying vainly to help myself, I could hear the heavy gates clank shut behind me. This was just in case the inner court should be defiled by a murder. In the minds of these fanatics, the murder of a heretic didn't matter much as long as it was committed *outside* the Holy Place.

Suddenly I heard a welcome cry which was to signal my escape.

"The soldiers are coming!" somebody shouted from the back of the crowd.

Another and another took it up.

"The soldiers are coming! The soldiers are coming!"

My assailants all drew back, disgruntled, and I sank stunned to the ground.

"Who is this man? What has he done?" I could hear the officer in the plume of chief captain enquiring.

He shook his head at the babble of noise that was offered to him in the form of an answer. It made absolutely no sense to him. In fact the only sensible words anybody could hear at that moment came in the mob chant, which had merely reduced from a howl to a hiss.

"Kill him! Kill him! Kill him!"

Unable to solve the situation there and then, Lysias, the commander, turned to his soldiers and ordered them to bind me and take me up into the fortress for questioning.

The soldiers duly clamped chains on my wrists and attempted to guarantee me safe passage through the crowd which was still screaming for my blood. At one stage the soldiers had to lift me shoulder high above the hysterical mob to keep them at bay.

When we had reached the relative safety of the steps up to the Roman fortress of Antonio which overlooked the temple courts, I turned to the captain and asked, "Can I have a word with you?"

The captain stood open-mouthed for a moment. He seemed startled to be addressed in Greek by somebody whom he assumed to be an outcast Jewish criminal.

"Can you speak Greek?" he enquired in amazement. "Then you are not that Egyptian who led four thousand brigands out into the desert."

"No, I am not," I was happy to inform him. "I am a Jew, a native of Tarsus in Cilicia. I am a citizen of no mean city. Please let me speak to these people."

I gathered from the puzzled look on his face that he regarded that as rather an odd request. Who in his right mind would want to speak to a lynch mob? Regardless of what he felt about it, however, he gave me permission and ordered a soldier to release one of my wrists.

I must have looked funny standing at the top of those steps, stretching out my one free hand in a gesture to a crowd who literally minutes earlier had been about to beat me to death. My upper lip was swollen and stiff, blood had begun to trickle down my cheek from a cut over my left eye, and my clothes were ripped and torn and stained with dust and blood.

Yet astonishingly, when I began to speak to them in a local Hebrew dialect, the crowd fell suddenly silent.

And I laid it on for them too. I had been a respected rabbi in that city once so by way of introduction I majored on my Jewish identity. I let them know that I was a Jew, who had been born in Tarsus, brought up in Jerusalem, trained by Gamaliel, and had once been an exponent of the Law and the Prophets, and a former member of the Sanhedrin.

The more I talked, the more attentive they became. When satisfied that I had established my credentials with them, I then told them of my conversion outside Damascus, taking care to mention Ananias, whom many of the older of my audience would have instantly recognised as a respected Jewish teacher.

Then I recounted the vision God had given me in the temple, revealing that the Jewish people would not accept the Lord Jesus, whom I had come to love and serve, as their Messiah, or their Saviour. I was therefore to leave Jerusalem and go far and wide, preaching the good news of free salvation to the Gentiles.

The crowd in the court below had listened with reasonably rapt attention up until that point but at the mention of the word 'Gentiles' pandemonium broke out once more.

To add insult to injury not only had I claimed that God had sent me to preach to the 'heathen dogs' of the Gentiles, but I had the absolute audacity to allege that the God of their fathers had given me such a preposterous revelation in their holy temple!

A totally baffled captain Lysias, who had not understood one single word of what I had been saying, looked down at the mob, who were by then howling more viciously than ever before. They were clawing the dust from the ground and flinging it up in the air. They were ripping the red and blue cloaks from around their own shoulders and hurling them in my direction.

It was, he probably reckoned, time to act.

He gave a curt word of command and I was pushed forward and another set of gates clanged shut behind me. At least I had now been saved from the clutches of the clamouring crowd, but as it turned out, I was not completely in the clear.

As he was about to leave he said to a centurion, "Let that prisoner be examined by torture until he confesses what he has done to so infuriate these Jews."

With that he left and I was led away.

The centurion wasted no time in obeying his master's command. In less than an hour I had been led out to a whipping post in the courtyard and was being tied up to it with strips of stiff leather.

I had already been lashed three times by Roman rods, and beaten five times with Jewish thongs, but examination by torture was a form of agony I did not fancy. This was the Roman method of wresting a confession from a recalcitrant prisoner, and involved being scourged with a whip made up of leather tipped thongs, the dreaded 'flagellum'.

Just before the lictors had finished tying me up I called across to their senior, the centurion in charge, "Is it lawful for you to scourge a Roman citizen without even giving him a trial?"

The centurion came across and studied me up and down, in complete silence. Then, obviously shocked, he growled to the lictors, "Don't touch that man until I come back," and hurried off.

It seemed only a matter of minutes until he returned with a very concerned looking Lysias just a stride or two behind.

The garrison commander pulled up stiffly in front of me, looked me straight in the eye, and asked gruffly, "Are *you* a Roman?"

"Yes," I replied, staring back at him, but I was forced to smile at the look of consternation on his face.

Lysias stood in silence for a few minutes, regarding me cynically. I could picture his mind working. He was looking at a pale, battered, dishevelled little man. How could this inconspicuous Jew possibly be a Roman citizen?

"I had to pay dearly for that privilege," he remarked, testing me.

At that point I simply couldn't resist an exercise in one-upmanship.

"Well I was free born," I replied. "My father was also a Roman citizen."

From that minute, everything changed. The chief captain knew that if I had been scourged he would have been in grave trouble so he acted immediately to make amends.

His first action was to order the astonished lictors to cut me free. Then he went over to the centurion and held a whispered consultation, before returning to me.

"I am keeping you in custody overnight as much for your own safety as for anything else," he explained. "If I released you to that mob out there, in the mood they are in at the moment, they would pull you apart."

Then turning to go he added, "And I will decide what to do with you in the morning."

At least I could be sure of a night's peace and protection.

That would give me time to reflect on the action and prediction of Agabus.

And pray earnestly to God for guidance in the morning, whatever happened.

For His will, I was still sure, would be done.

Chapter Twenty-One

A REAL SLAP IN THE TEETH

By mid-morning of the following day I realized how Lysias had decided to solve his problem.

Two soldiers came into my cell and marched me from there down the stone steps again, out of the Roman fortress and back into the Jewish domain. I was led to one of the outer rooms of the temple, where the Sanhedrin had been ordered to assemble.

It appeared that the chief captain had summoned them to see if they could make any sense of my case, or at least give him some explanation as to what had so incensed the Jewish mob the day before.

When paraded up before them I recognised some of the Pharisees who had been my fellow-students in the class of Gamaliel in the House of Interpretation, so many years before. The setting brought back a host of memories of days gone past, and since I had once been a member of that Jewish final court of appeal myself, when I was invited to speak I addressed the gathered company, not formally as, 'rulers and elders of the House of Israel', but as 'brothers'.

Confident that I could give an honest account of myself, and all that God had done in and through me, I opened what I had hoped would be a full and fair hearing with the words, "Brothers I have lived with a perfectly clear conscience before God right up until this present day."

Then before I could utter another word, a man who appeared to have been galled by either the intimacy or the honesty of my approach, yelled, "Hit that man a slap on the mouth!"

And quick as a flash one of the temple guards obeyed his order.

I lost my temper, and my self-control, for one anguished second.

The pain of that unexpected blow on my tender mouth, which was still swollen from the punching of the previous day, and its daunting effect on my personal pride, caused me to retort immediately. And aggressively.

"God will judge you, you whitewashed wall!" I bawled back. "You are sitting there to judge me by the law, and you can't even keep the law. For you have just commanded that I should be struck!"

There was a sharp intake of breath from some of the spectators who always seemed to turn up at the Sanhedrin sessions.

"How dare you shout at the High Priest like that?" one of them roared, indignantly.

It was an offence to berate the High Priest, and nobody knew that better than me.

That day, though, with my failing eyesight I hadn't recognised the man who had ordered the blatant and quite illegal violation of my Jewish rights, as the High Priest. And I was sorry for my mistake but not for him. I didn't mind confronting an unscrupulous hypocrite, as Ananias was reputed to have been, but I would never intentionally break the holy law of God.

Yet the altercation with that hostile High Priest had placed me in an unenviable position.

There was no way that I was going to be afforded a sympathetic hearing before those men, so I resorted to a ruse to divert attention away from myself.

From my earlier associations with the Council of Seventy I was well aware that the two factions within the Jewish leadership, the Pharisees and the Sadducees, had always been at loggerheads on particular points of doctrine. And one of the issues on which they could never seem to agree was the resurrection of the dead.

The Pharisees believed in it. The Sadducees didn't.

Since the resurrection of my Lord from the dead, and eternal life after physical death for the believer, had formed a fundamental part of my preaching down the years, I chose that particular moment to present it as a case in my defence.

Referring back to my earlier training I coupled it with my current beliefs and called out above the rising tide of angry voices, " My brothers, I am a Pharisee and the son of a Pharisee! I am on trial here today because of my hope in the resurrection of the dead!"

That proclamation did the trick! Suddenly I had half of the Sanhedrin on my side!

Soon the learned leaders of our nation were at each throats. And all I had to do was stand and watch!

Whenever some of the Sadducees left their seats and came rushing towards me, Lysias intervened again, sending four soldiers to drag me away. The chief captain was by then even more confused than ever.

For half of the men who had started off opposing me were now supporting me, and a sombre meeting of the august religious ruling body had degenerated into an absolute madhouse!

In less than five minutes they had me up the outside steps once more and returned to the only location in which I would be safe in all Jerusalem. And that was the fortress of the 'foreign oppressor'!

As that day wore on I began to feel very much alone.

The barracks of the Roman garrison were cold and comfortless, and although thankful that I had been isolated from my Jewish enemies, I was heartbroken to be separated from my Christian friends.

What was to become of me?

Was I to end my days here, in Jerusalem?

There were so many doubts, so many questions.

Then in the silence of the night the Lord revealed Himself to me in a vision. He appeared to quell my nagging fears and to strengthen me, as He had done so often, when I had felt so low, before.

"Cheer up, Paul, don't be afraid!" He told me very clearly. "As you have borne fearless witness to Me in Jerusalem, you must do the same in Rome."

It was great to have the Lord, and be comforted by His abiding presence in times of trial. In times of quiet reflection I could look away above the heads of Jewish priests and Roman captains, cantankerous Christians and howling mobs, and see Jesus.

He would always be there for me, and He was the only one I had to please.

I could depend on Him for grace, guidance and help.

And since He had assured me that I was going to bear witness to Him in Rome that was enough for me.

I didn't need to know how, or when.

I just slept soundly for the rest of the night.

It was great to wake up in the assurance that the will of God would be done, and that I would some day realize my cherished ambition to visit Rome. And for the first half of the next day I basked in the comforting afterglow of the vision of the night before.

Unfortunately that didn't last long.

Just after midday I had an agitated and anxious visitor.

It was my nephew and I was pleasantly surprised to see him. He was a student in the city as I had once been myself, and although still very much an orthodox Jew, his natural ties had proved stronger than his religious convictions. For he came to warn his uncle, who had 'deserted the faith of the fathers', about something he had heard in the temple that very morning.

"Uncle Paul, your life is still in danger," he began, breathlessly. "A crowd of about forty men have vowed neither to eat or drink until they have killed you. I heard them scheming in the temple. They had just come from asking the leaders of the Sanhedrin to request another meeting with you tomorrow morning. Then when you are brought out of the security of this castle they are planning an ambush to murder you."

When he stopped to wipe the perspiration from himself, and take a few deep breaths, I called a centurion over.

"Take this lad to the chief captain," I told him. "He has something important to tell him."

The centurion agreed to do so and when my nephew had composed himself sufficiently both of them disappeared along the echoing stone corridor.

They seemed to be away for ages but eventually they came back. My young nephew was eager to get out of the fortress as soon as possible because he thought his fellow-students would be sending out a search party for him and he couldn't very well explain to them where he had been! Before hurrying off, however, he told me that Lysias had taken him aside and listened carefully to all he had to say. The commander had been most sympathetic, but was now considering what to do next!

I'm sure that man often wished he had just let the Jews hammer me to death on any one of the three times they had already tried it!

There were two basic points for him to consider, and they both related to the future safety of two people, literally him and me.

His concern about these matters, and his conclusion as to how best resolve them, came in a visit he made to my cell shortly after nightfall.

"Be prepared to travel at nine o'clock tonight, Paul," he instructed. "For some reason which is beyond me to understand, the Jews in this city are intent upon killing you, so you will never be safe here. Since you are a Roman citizen, and in my custody, it is my duty to ensure that you are kept safe and given a fair trial. As you will know, a Roman officer could be severely punished for losing a prisoner in his charge.

So what I am proposing is to transfer you, now, by night, to Caesarea and place you in the care of Felix, the Governor of this entire district. You will be safe and secure there."

With that he smiled briefly, turned sharply, and walked stiffly away, possibly to make final arrangements for the journey.

I was quite astounded when I was led down into the courtyard of the castle, shortly before nine o'clock. The place was jam packed with soldiers, in full battle dress, both footmen and spearmen, drawn up rank by rank. There were four hundred of them in all! Lysias certainly wasn't going to risk his life by losing me!

Then just outside the castle gate were seventy cavalrymen, the hooves of their horses clicking on the cobbles. And just inside the gate, in the shelter of an archway, were two horses, which had been prepared for me, Paul, the prisoner. They must have been expecting a fast trip for they had supplied me with an extra mount!

When I was safely seated on one of the horses, an officer at the head of the cavalry troop gave a curt command and we moved off, as fast as marching men could march, through the silent city streets.

As the great northern gates in the city walls were swung open to let our mini-army out my mind drifted away back to another time I had gone out through those gates. I had been in charge of a unit of the Jewish temple guards at that time, on my way to Damascus to capture Christians and possibly murder them. On the night in question I was a captive Christian surrounded by virtually half of the Roman soldiers stationed in Jerusalem, to prevent the Jews from the temple from murdering me!

How things had changed!

The centurion in charge of that all-night march kept pressing northward through the mountain passes, and then shortly after midnight we veered off westward towards the Great Sea.

Dawn was breaking behind us as we descended on to the fertile Plain of Sharon. Here the road cut a swathe through the fields of wheat and barley which were almost ripe and which swished and swayed softly in the early morning breeze.

The garrison town of Antipatris was just coming alive for another day when we entered it, and when we arrived at the Roman camp there the four hundred foot soldiers were given some time to rest before returning to Jerusalem. Since we had passed safely through the mountain region, notorious for its robber bands, and since I was far enough away from fanatical Jews to be considered out of danger, it was reckoned that the foot soldiers could be best deployed back in the capital.

The horsemen stayed with me though, and after resting both ourselves and our horses in Antipatris we made the journey across the coastal plain at a canter, clouds of choking dust trailing out behind us. And in mid-afternoon a travel weary group arrived in Caesarea.

We had no time to rest there, however. The centurion was obviously anxious to be safely rid of his charge so we made straight for the Roman citadel, which had once been the palace of Herod the Great.

When we had dismounted I was immediately marched into the presence of the Procurator, and the centurion pulled a scroll from the folds of his tunic and handed it to Felix who unrolled it and began to read,

'Greetings from Claudius Lysias to the most excellent Governor Felix.

This man was seized by the Jews who were about to kill him when I came along with a band of soldiers and saved him from them for I had learned that he was a Roman citizen…'

I had to smile at that, for Lysias seemed to have forgotten to mention that he had ordered to have me examined by torture before discovering that I was a Roman citizen!

The letter ended with Lysias very cleverly, but very graciously ridding himself of responsibility for me.

'This man has done nothing worthy of the death penalty or even prison, so when news reached me that the Jews were planning to ambush him I at once passed him on to you,' Felix was continuing to read out very formally. 'I have told his accusers to present their charges against him to you. Farewell.'

Felix rolled up the scroll and then looked directly down at me.

"From what province of the Empire do you come?" was his first question.

"I am from Cilicia," I told him.

"Very well then. You will be kept under guard here in Herod's Palace and when your accusers come down from Jerusalem, I will try your case," the Governor said, dismissing me from his presence for the present.

I was then led away to a room where I would be guarded night and day.

Just nine days earlier Agabus and my brethren had warned me in Caesarea against going up to the Holy City. I had ignored their counsel, and now I was back. And all I had to look forward to was the arrival of my 'accusers from Jerusalem'.

Or was it?

God had promised me when in Jerusalem that I would bear witness to him in Rome, and He always kept His promises.

And His will would always be done.

But how?

Chapter Twenty-Two

A PROPER PEST

It was five days before my accusers appeared, and during that time I was held under armed guard in Herod's Palace in Caesarea.

When the day of my hearing before Felix arrived, I was led in to find the haughty Roman governor seated on his marble chair, with Ananias, the High Priest from Jerusalem, my 'plastered sepulchre' of the previous encounter, and a number of the members of the Sanhedrin, both Pharisees and Sadducees, sitting smugly nearby.

They had hired an eminent Jewish lawyer called Tertullus, and appeared curiously confident that they could win the case they had chosen to bring against me.

Following the court preliminaries Tertullus began his presentation with a sickeningly insincere introduction, extolling the merits of Felix the Procurator, who had, he said, brought them 'unbroken peace' in that part of Palestine. That sounded rather odd to me. Why, I wondered, if this peace was so perfect, had it needed four hundred and seventy Roman soldiers to escort a poor little solitary soul like me from Jerusalem to Caesarea?!

Felix waved a hand impatiently to indicate to the lawyer that he should forgo the false and futile flattery and proceed with the business on hand.

This Tertullus proceeded to do with some gusto, detailing his three charges against me, any one of which he thought should have seen me convicted.

"This proper pest," he began, pointing an accusing finger directly at me, as though I was some horrible, insignificant, slimy slug, " has caused the Jews to rebel all over the Roman Empire, is a ringleader of the sect of the Nazarenes, and has attempted to profane the temple."

So that was it.

My crimes, according to counsel for the prosecution, were treason against the Emperor, heresy in relation to the Jewish religion, and sacrilege, for profaning the temple.

As he went on, though, to claim that they were about to give me a fair trial, when in actual fact they were in the process of giving me a fair hiding, when Lysias and his men snatched me away from them 'with great force', I was seriously tempted to interrupt the man.

What absolute nonsense! What patent lies!

On completion of his inaccurate accusations Tertullus stepped back to calls of assent from the travelling Jewish party.

"Well done, Tertullus!" someone shouted.

"That's all true!" another went on, and one by one they took it up.

Then Felix, who I could see was growing progressively impatient with this vocal support, and was also becoming increasingly wary of being caught up in some squabble about the Jewish law, as Lysias had indicated in his letter, flung me an arrogant nod. This action had a dual effect. It silenced the shouts of support for Tertullus and it also indicated that I was at liberty to conduct my own defence.

When stepping forward to address the governor I did not feel disposed to flatter Felix, who had a rather unsavoury reputation, but I paid respect to his years of experience and then proceeded to counter the claims made against me, one by one.

I began by explaining that I had only been a short time in Jerusalem and that I certainly had not caused any disturbance there.

To refute the charge of heresy I pointed out that I had never given up my belief in the Law and the Prophets, and in keeping with their teachings I held the doctrine of the resurrection, which some of my accusers also believed. In addition to an affirmation of my beliefs I also thought it essential to draw the court's attention to the fact that as far as practical living was concerned I had endeavoured to live conscientiously before the God of my Fathers all the days of my life.

The allegation of sacrilege was totally unfounded, I told them, since I had come to Jerusalem to bring gifts for the poor and needy and when my accusers had set upon me in the temple I had actually been there to observe one of its strictest ceremonies!

Then I seized upon what I reckoned to be the weakest point of the case for the prosecution, and my strongest line of defence.

"And what about these Jews from Asia who accused me of desecration?" I enquired, scathingly. Having gazed slowly all around, as though to conduct a thorough search for them, I went on, "Where are they? Why have they not been brought here to witness against me?"

To round off, I looked straight at Ananias, and then one by one around the others who sat staring back at me, the hatred simmering in their surly eyes.

"Or perhaps my accusers here would like to state if they found me guilty of any offence when I appeared before them in Jerusalem, except that half of them were mad at me for declaring my firm belief in the resurrection of the dead," I said, before retreating backwards, to indicate that I had finished.

God had helped me in that hostile situation.

I was being accused by unscrupulous Jewish fanatics, before a singularly unprincipled Roman judge, but I had a clear conscience before God and my nation. And when I had rested my case everybody else had more to worry about than me!

The Jerusalem contingent were gazing fiercely and fixedly at Felix, awaiting his judgement, but when it came, it was not to their pleasing.

Ignoring their impatience, the Procurator reread the letter from Lysias, which had been lying in his lap throughout the trial, and the thought of the man who had sent me to Caesarea to be tried, must have given him an idea.

I could sense that he had judged that I was innocent of any crime against anybody, but he dare not release me for this would not only antagonise the Jews but also put my life in danger. So he opted for the compromise.

"When Colonel Lysias comes down from Jerusalem I will hear what he has to say, and then make a final decision on the matter," he announced.

Then turning to a centurion he said, "I order that this man be kept in military custody. He is to have every privilege possible and his friends are to be granted unlimited access to his quarters."

The Jews returned to Jerusalem disappointed. They hadn't got their man.

Felix returned to his apartment in the palace, frustrated. He had been left with their man.

I was released from cell dwelling to reside in a more pleasant room with two armed soldiers on guard outside my door, twenty four hours a day. And there I was content to await the next command from my Heavenly Headquarters.

In the days following the trial, two things happened in quick succession.

The first of these was that Luke and Aristarchus arrived from Jerusalem. Philip from Caesarea had presumably sent them news that I was now free to have my friends to visit, and they came immediately and took lodgings in the city. It was wonderful to see them again, especially Luke, who was constantly concerned for my physical well being.

The other significant, and I suppose to some extent surprising event of those early days under house arrest, was the invitation to go to speak to Felix and his wife Drusilla, one day.

Drusilla was a young Jewish princess who had been persuaded to leave her husband to marry the scheming Felix, and when she had heard about me, she told her husband that she would like to see me and hear what I had to say.

This gave me an unexpected opportunity to preach the Gospel.

When I was led forward to stand before them I found Felix, who had been born in slavery, sitting robed in the purple and white of a Roman governor, and beside him his beautiful twenty year old wife who was interested in nothing but pleasure, and in nobody but herself. On this occasion, however, I was present not as a prisoner before a court, but as a guest exponent of the Christian faith in the luxury of a lavish reception room.

As I began to tell them of God and His love, of the death of Christ, and of the resurrection of the dead, I was agreeably surprised at how much they both knew about the way of salvation already, and how interested they appeared to be in my explanation of it.

I was glad to have the chance to show them that the Gospel of Jesus Christ was not just a theoretical religion, however, but that it could be of everlasting benefit to all those who believe. I showed them from the Jewish scriptures, with which Drusilla should have been familiar, that the peasant preacher from Galilee was in fact the promised Messiah, and that through faith in His atoning death on Calvary we could be cleansed from the guilt of all our sin.

And sin was something that Felix knew plenty about.

He had been procurator in Palestine for eight years, and the record of his rule read like a long litany of greed and treachery, lust and blood, murdered men and dishonoured women.

That was a marvellous moment, which had been granted to me only by God, and I tried, with His help to make the most of it.

When I had been speaking for well over an hour, telling the Roman governor and his Jewish bride of the need for the righteousness that only came through faith in Christ, of the possibility of personal and moral purity through commitment to Him, and of the certainty of the judgement of God to come upon our sins, Felix began to tremble. He tried bravely to disguise it but I could see his arms shaking where he had them hidden in the folds of his robe.

Drusilla must have sensed this, too, and she became rather uneasy. Her initial interest had disappeared. Having a famous preacher prisoner along for a little intellectual entertainment on a long boring afternoon was one thing, but to see her profligate husband upset by his direct challenges was something else. She had no notion of forsaking her lavish lifestyle to follow some crucified carpenter, and she would help ensure that her husband didn't either.

Felix became conscious of her overplayed unease, and was possibly glad of an excuse to dismiss me, for I could feel that God was dealing very definitely with him. He uncovered an arm, raised a hand to stop me in full flow, and said, "That will do for now, Paul. When I have a suitable time some other day I will call for you and we can talk again."

We did talk again in the weeks and months that ran into years that followed, but never again did Felix show any interest in his sin, his soul, or his salvation. When we met he would talk about anything else and he appeared interested in my travels across the Empire and would ask many questions about places like Ephesus and Athens, Philippi and Corinth. His main objective in inviting me to call and chat to him was, I was soon set to discover, a less than honourable one.

Felix had somehow found out that the alms, which I had brought to Jerusalem, and which I had mentioned in my defence before him, had amounted to quite a considerable sum of money. When he added to that the fact that one of my best friends was a doctor and that Philip and some of the other local Christians seemed to be reasonably well off, Felix thought he smelt money amongst us.

During one of our consultations he hinted that I should not consider my freedom an impossible dream, for this could 'probably be arranged for a suitable fee.' Such an 'arrangement' would constitute a flagrant violation of Roman law but I had long since learnt that Felix paid little regard to such considerations.

For my part, though, I was being detained for alleged crimes which I had never committed, so I saw no reason to break the law, and dishonour my Christian witness, to obtain a freedom which should have been mine by right.

I paid the penalty of a pure conscience by wearing my chain.

This was the chain I had to wear when out of doors. My refusal to bribe Felix to release me resulted in a long stay in prison. One of the few pleasures of those days of confinement, though, was my walks through the city streets or along the wide beaches on the shore of the sometimes roaring and sometimes rippling Great Sea, with Luke or some other faithful friend.

There were times, too, when I strolled, chained to a soldier, down by the harbour to watch the boats load up and set sail for Rome. As they disappeared below the rim of the western horizon I often wondered how long it would be until I was aboard one of them. My Lord had promised me that I would witness to Him in the Imperial Capital so I knew it was not a question of *if*, but **when**, I went.

We didn't waste our time in the evenings, either. Many of the members of the church in Caesarea, including Philip and his daughters, came regularly to see me. They used to bring me occasional treats to eat, but more importantly they brought encouraging tidings of the progress of the work of God both at home and abroad. In those evening sessions we spent many hours praising God and in the study of the Scriptures, and prayer.

I found Luke's company particularly comforting during that two year enforced stay in Caesarea. For in addition to the medical attention he gave me, I derived a great mental and spiritual stimulus from talking through with him some aspects of a personal project he had embarked upon.

Luke had a friend called Theophilus and he had undertaken to write down for him a full account of the life of our Lord. When in Jerusalem, before coming down to Caesarea to be with me, he had been busying himself gathering all sorts of material from the believers who had been present in the city, and who had been closely associated with the Saviour, during His days on earth. We spent many profitable walking out or sitting in hours, enjoying the warmth of close fellowship with our Lord, as he read to me snippets of what he had written, and we discussed them together.

He often sat for hours, too, quizzing me about my experiences and trips when he hadn't been with me. That, he used to tell me as he took copious notes on rolls of parchment, was for another idea he had up ahead. When he had finished his comprehensive record of the birth and life, death and resurrection, deeds and words of Jesus he was then proposing to write the essential sequel to it. Part two, as he planned it, would provide an in-depth account of the formation and growth of the early church.

Some task! I often told him, but he kept assuring me that he believed that God would help him. And I had no choice but to tell him that he was right!

It was great to have the company of Luke, Aristarchus and Philip during the day throughout my stay in Caesarea, but the nights there were often lonely. And often noisy!

There was constant bickering between the Jews and Greeks in that city, as to who actually owned the city. The Jews claimed it as theirs for Herod had given it to them, and the Syrian Greeks claimed it as theirs, since it had belonged to their forefathers long before Herod had ever been heard of, and until he had wrested it from them!

These civil rights disputes often ended in running battles in the streets. The soldiers from the Roman garrison had no love for, and consequently showed no mercy towards, the passionate Jewish activists when called upon to quell these regular riots. There were many nights when I found it impossible to sleep for the clang of steel upon steel and the shouts of anguish as the streets of Caesarea ran with the blood of both Jews and Greeks.

In a peculiar way this civil unrest sparked off a sequence of events which led eventually to some movement in my position.

The Jews, not only in that city, but also from other parts of Palestine made a formal complaint to Caesar Augustus in Rome about Felix's perceived bias against them and consequent maltreatment of them. This in turn led to the recall of the rogue governor to the capital to answer the charges laid against him.

Since Felix dared not further infuriate the Jews before leaving, however, he left me still a prisoner to await my fate at the hands of his successor.

Festus, the new governor, proved to be a much more principled man than his predecessor, and he took an immediate interest in my case. As part of his inaugural tour of his new province he visited Jerusalem where he was at once bombarded by requests to have me returned to Jerusalem for trial.

Sensing, perhaps from the mood of the Jews, that this might not be in the interests of the best traditions of Roman justice, he insisted that if the Jews had anything against me they should come to Caesarea and present their case before him there.

The Jews, feeling that they could wring concessions from the new man who might be anxious to make a big impression, agreed to do that, and we went through the whole performance again.

Although Ananias had been replaced as High Priest by an equally bitter man called Ishmael, and although they had not thought fit to hire a barrister to present their case second time around, nothing else had changed.

I was charged with exactly the same offences, treason, heresy and sacrilege, and I rebutted them before Festus as I had done before Felix, dealing with them, and disproving them, singly as they came.

Festus was flummoxed.

He realized immediately that he was being confronted with issues concerning a 'weird 'Jewish religion. It was something to do, he gathered, with a man called Jesus who had died and who, I was claiming, had risen from the dead! Such matters were far and away beyond the scope of his experience, so in his naivety he thought he had the solution to everyone's problems when he asked me, "Are you willing to go up to Jerusalem to be tried there?"

I could almost see the eyes of the Jewish delegation light up at that.

If I consented to go up to the Holy City I would probably never make it, I knew, for I was quite sure that Festus would not realize the gravity of my position and send nearly five hundred soldiers to protect me, as Lysias had done. And a well planned ambush in a mountain pass could see me disposed of forever.

I knew something else, however. I was well aware that a Roman judge could not move a case to another court without the consent of the accused, and so my answer to his question was a simple, "No."

Then, guided I believe by God, and realizing that I could hope for nothing more from High Priests or Procurators, I claimed the last right of a Roman citizen.

Fixing Festus with my gaze, I said, "I stand at Caesar's judgment seat where I ought to be judged. I am a Roman citizen, and I have done no wrong to the Jews, as you very well know. If I have done anything worthy of death, I am not afraid to die, but if none of the accusations that these men are making are true then you cannot hand me over to them."

I paused for a moment at that point to let the import of what I had just said sink in, before opening my last option.

"I appeal to Caesar!" I announced, raising my voice so that all could hear.

There were gasps of astonishment from Festus and some of his counsellors.

Their prisoner had appealed to have his case taken out of their jurisdiction, but it was an appeal that they knew full well they couldn't ignore.

The governor's legal advisers held a hurried and huddled meeting at the back of the judgement hall and in less than ten minutes Festus had returned to give their verdict.

It was probably a kind of a rebuff for him to have his first case in his new job taken out of his hands, but I saw it as my only chance of fair treatment in the days ahead.

Thus it was a possibly slightly peeved Festus who announced, much to the disgust of the greatly peeved Jews, "You have appealed to Caesar! And to Caesar you will go!"

It wasn't just exactly as I would have planned it, but I knew from the prophet Isaiah that God's ways are not our ways, and whatever the circumstances I would soon be on the first leg of my journey to Rome.

At last.

Chapter Twenty-Three

WHAT AM I GOING TO WRITE?

Caesarea was gripped by a carnival atmosphere just a few days after my trial before Festus.

When I asked Philip what was going on he informed me that apparently King Herod Agrippa and his sister Bernice had come to greet and congratulate the new governor. Festus, in turn, pleased to have the attention of some notable, if not very powerful, Jewish public figures, had arranged a five-day festival programme in their honour.

I enjoyed the buzz about the city.

The fact that most people appeared to be in both cheerful and peaceful mood as they attended plays in the vast open-air marble theatre, and chariot races in the stadium, made a pleasant change from the Jews and Greeks battling it out unto blood on the streets, under Felix.

As we took our daily walk through the streets of the city, with me still chained to a soldier, Luke, Aristarchus and I enjoyed watching the multitudes of people thronging to and fro.

Then late one evening a centurion came along to the room where I was being held, with a specific summons.

"You are to appear before the governor and his guests tomorrow in the Hall of Hearing, Paul," he announced. "His Excellency has informed me that King Agrippa would like to hear what you have to say."

Paul the Prisoner had been invited to star in a Royal Command Performance!

Wonderful!

God who had promised that I would bear His Name before kings, governors and chief captains had arranged for me to have an audience with the puppet King of Trachonitis and his widowed sister!

And I would make the most of it!

Early next afternoon I was escorted down to a small side room off the Hall of Hearing, and from there I could hear the sound of the tramp of hundreds of marching feet and an occasional fanfare of trumpets.

The crowds were packing in for my guest appearance!

Then slowly and gradually the hubbub subsided and after a few minutes a centurion appeared through the doorway and signalled to my guard that I was to be brought out.

As I was led by my shackle across to an appointed spot on the floor, directly in front of the raised dais at one end of the Hall, I was momentarily taken aback by the array of pomp before me.

Agrippa and Bernice were both dressed in flowing robes of royal purple and had gold circlet crowns sitting forward on their foreheads. They were attended by a suite of servants in extremely colourful silk costumes bedecked with jewels.

Festus sat beside Agrippa whom he had placed in the middle as the chief guest. The recently appointed governor looked distinctive in the scarlet robe of Roman Procurator, and he was escorted by a retinue of lictors and bodyguards who stood at arms behind the three gilded chairs, which he had provided for his guests and himself.

On either side of the main platform party, and in only slightly less prominent positions, sat a number of the local city dignitaries in their robes of office, and the hall was flanked down either side by row upon row of Roman soldiers from the higher ranks, all resplendent in shining armour. I had come to know a large number of these men during my two-year stay in Caesarea, and had spoken to many of them of the Saviour when we had been literally chained together.

A quick glance behind showed me that the public gallery was also crammed to capacity, so I could rest assured that I would not be totally without support in those imposing, but pagan surroundings. Some of the local believers would be in that crowd. Luke, too, would be shoved in somewhere to make even more notes for his ever-growing pile!

The expectant crowd fell into a hushed silence as Festus opened the proceedings with an attempt to explain the purpose of the grandiose gathering.

"King Agrippa and all others here present," he began, and then paused to point briefly at me. I felt rather conspicuous in the plain robe and wrist chain of a prisoner amidst all the encircling pomp and grandeur, as he went on, in his very best official voice, "You see this man! The Jews keep screaming at me that he is not fit to live, but I have tried him and found him not guilty of anything deserving the death penalty. He has appealed to Caesar but before I send him to Rome I have to write down the crimes of which he stands accused. And my big problem is, what am I going to write? Perhaps you could examine him, Agrippa, and identify some sustainable charge I could put in writing. It is going to look a bit ridiculous if I send him to be judged before the Emperor without indicating the charges laid against him!"

What a confession to have to make! I thought.

From that moment on, King Agrippa, who was seated centre stage, took control.

He looked down at me, and with an overdone air of importance, said, "You are permitted to speak for yourself."

I needed no second bidding. An open door had been set before me, and I was determined to walk straight through it!

Lifting my hand, in a habit of mine at the start of any address, I stretched it forward, giving my minder a sharp jolt by tugging on the chain that joined us.

It would be unwise, I decided, to launch into my main objective for that speech, which was to challenge my august audience with the claims of Jesus Christ, without first filling them in on my chequered career to date. Thus, after the preliminary courtesies, I began by telling them of my early days in Jerusalem, and my training and teachings as a Pharisee, including my belief in the resurrection of the dead.

Having traced my Jewish upbringing I then proceeded to outline one of the results of that upbringing, which was my fanatical persecution of the 'sect of the Nazarenes'.

I could see some eyebrows raised as I described in detail the lengths to which I had gone in an attempt to exterminate the hated 'Way'. How, I almost imagined them wondering, did this man ever become a follower of Jesus Christ?

It was an understandable reaction from anyone who had any knowledge of Jewish history, so I went on to give them a graphic account of my turning point, blinded by light and face down in the dust, outside Damascus. That was the moment when the crucified and resurrected Lord Jesus had appeared to me in person, challenging me about my behaviour and unbelief and instructing me to follow Him.

My story seemed to have grabbed everyone's attention by that time.

I noticed that several of the Roman dignitaries who had come to my guest appearance in the Festus Festival with a supercilious sneering attitude, were by then listening intently.

The columns of soldiers stood stock-still.

Nobody spoke, shuffled or shifted in the jam-packed gallery behind me.

From my dramatic conversion I went on to tell of my Divine commission.

God had made it clear to me, I told them, that I was to be His special envoy to the Gentiles, to turn them from darkness to light, and from the power of Satan to Himself.

Since I was approaching a crucial stage in my defence I then addressed Agrippa specifically, informing him that the greater part of my life had been spent in the humble execution of that Heavenly commission. I had devoted every day that God had sent me to the spread of His gospel to both Jew and Gentile, and that was the sole reason why the offended Jews had seized me in the temple.

Being quite convinced that Agrippa must have, at some stage in his thirty-three years, come in contact with the Jewish scriptures, I pointed out to him that I wasn't teaching anything other than what Moses and the prophets had predicted.

The sacred writings had foretold that The Messiah, the Christ, should suffer, and Jesus had suffered on the cross of Calvary. The Promised One should also rise from the dead, and Jesus had been resurrected and seen by many, three days after His death.

And it was the message of salvation through faith in Him, which I had been commanded to preach, that carried the only hope of both light and peace for both Jew and Gentile.

At that point the hush in the Hall of Hearing was suddenly shattered.

Festus, the Roman governor, and host of the ostentatious occasion, could take no more.

Whether he had been challenged by his first ever encounter with the truth of the Christian gospel, and didn't want to hear any more of it, or whether he just saw me as some sort of an unbalanced enthusiast, I couldn't quite be sure, but I rather fancied the latter.

To him I was little more than an avid reader and thinker, whose guarded room in the Palace housed a two-year accumulation of books and parchments of an obscure religious nature. And no matter when he happened to see me I always seemed to be in deep discussion with cultured companions!

Now, there I was, standing before him, insulting his practical Roman intelligence by giving an impassioned account of visions and revelations, of ancient prophecies, and of some Jewish Prophet who had been crucified and then had risen from the dead and was Divine, and who could forgive sins and dispel the darkness of the Jews as well as the Gentiles!

That was far too far for Festus.

"Paul! Paul! You are out of your mind!" he shouted, much to the astonishment of my captive audience. "All your learning has driven you mad!"

I was nonplussed for a moment.

It had been going well, everyone had seemed so interested, and now I had been interrupted.

The man before me was, nonetheless, the Roman Procurator, and it was my duty to treat him with respect.

Looking up at him I replied, with perfect God-granted composure, "I am not mad, most noble Festus. What I have been telling you is both true and reasonable."

Then nodding towards Agrippa I went on, "The King here knows what I am talking about, and I can speak freely before him. These matters cannot have escaped his attention at one time or another, for this was no undercover operation. In fact the crucifixion and resurrection of Christ rocked this country to its roots during Pilate's jurisdiction, less than thirty years ago!"

The scarlet-clad governor obviously hadn't appreciated what I had been talking about but since I was firmly convinced that the purple-clad King had, I turned my attentions to him.

It was time to close in on the issue of personal commitment, so I challenged Agrippa to make some response to what I had been talking about.

"King Agrippa, do you believe the Prophets?" I asked him, directly, before adding, "I know you do!"

There were gasps from the gallery behind me.

Those of them who attended every public hearing possible had never seen the tables turned before, with the prisoner assuming the role of interrogator. And the Jews amongst them were amazed that any person, and particularly a prisoner, should presume to address His Royal Highness with such perceived impertinence.

My question did what it was designed to do, and that was place Agrippa in a position where he would be forced to gave me an answer of some sort.

It would be hard for him, though, since either a simple 'Yes' on 'No' to my enquiry, would present him with a major difficulty.

If he said 'no' the Jews present would be up in arms at their King denying belief in the sacred Scriptures.

If, on the other hand, he said 'Yes', he knew quite well that my next question was bound to be, "Why then do you not believe that

Jesus Christ is the Son of God, The Anointed One, the Promised Messiah, The Hope of Israel?"

It was an embarrassing predicament for him.

I could almost sense him squirming as he retorted, after a brief but awkward interval, "In a short time you will be making me into a Christian!"

The gallery gasped again, and a babble of conversation rippled round the Hall, which had been wreathed in sombre silence for so long.

What did the King mean?

Had he intended his crisp riposte to be a light-hearted joke, a bitter sarcasm or an explosion of anger? Or was it even, perhaps, the sincere confession of a convicted conscience?

My only option was to assume that his reply was a genuine statement of fact, and I followed it up as such.

"Short time or long, " I began, echoing his words, "I pray God that not only you but everybody else who is listening to me here today may become as I am..."

I could see the mouths of some of my audience fall open at that remark. Perhaps they had mistaken me. I had wished for them the inner joy and peace that I enjoyed in Christ Jesus, not my outward position as a prisoner.

To qualify that last remark I gave my minder a second start by raising my right arm, jangling my chain and adding, "Except these chains!"

By that time, though, Agrippa was on his feet, to signify that the hearing was over, and the court was closed. He obviously didn't want to hear any more, or be asked any further compromising questions.

He led the way out of the Hall, followed by Bernice, and Festus was left to bring up the rear. A host of eager, dutiful slaves and attendants hastened hotfoot to keep up.

Later that night a friendly centurion told me that he had overheard them discussing my case at the evening banquet, and that Festus had restated his opinion that I had done nothing worthy of death or even of chains. Agrippa, he reported, had gone even further by asserting that I could have been released if I hadn't appealed to the Emperor.

That judgement was of little use to me, though, by then.

The appeal had been made and I was happy to be on my way to Rome.

Festus, at the same time, had been left with an even bigger problem.

And Agrippa had been very little help to him.

What was he going to write, *now*?

Chapter Twenty-Four

I BELIEVE GOD

Nevertheless, Festus must have conferred with his legal team and concocted something, for about four days later I had an unexpected visitor to my room in Herod's Palace.

It was Julius, a centurion whom I had already met a number of times. This high-ranking officer was a member of The Emperor's Own Regiment, and he informed me that I was to make preparations for a trip to Rome under his command.

Julius had been briefed on my appeal to Caesar and had been present in Caesarea during my defence before Festus and Agrippa. He seemed a reasonable man and I asked him if I could be afforded, as was the entitlement of a Roman of rank, the services of two personal attendants on my journey to the capital. When he had granted my request I named Luke the physician, and Aristarchus the Thessalonian, as my servants. My two friends welcomed the opportunity to accompany me, whatever their job description. And my purpose in arranging their passage was to ensure that I was not left bereft of the comfort of constant Christian companionship. I didn't fancy making that journey alone, with nobody but heathen soldiers and sailors for company! Not after my Athens experience of a few years before!

Two days later we set sail from the harbour.

It was touching when almost the entire church in Caesarea turned up on the quayside to say their farewells. Some of them seemed upset at first, but when I told them that I was convinced that this was God's will for me, they appeared somewhat consoled.

The ship on which we were to complete the first leg of our trip was a coastal trading vessel bound for the ports of Asia Minor.

When Luke, Aristarchus and I had finished waving to our friends back on shore, I took a leisurely look around the crowded coaster.

Julius, with his armed band of soldiers had a few other prisoners to look after as well as myself. This rather despondent-looking group of men sat huddled together under close guard. These prisoners had not appealed to the emperor, but rather were being shipped to Rome to satisfy the emperor's insatiable appetite for gory pleasure. They were probably destined to fight wild animals, or each other, to the death, before bloodthirsty audiences in barbaric amphi-theatres.

That large group under the command of Julius, made up most of the ship's complement. There were a few other single passengers on board as well, and a sizeable ship's company, whose job it was to bring us on our way. Cargo of all kinds was stacked and stored in the hold, and in every available space on deck.

Our first port of call was Sidon, and I asked for permission to go ashore there. Since it was going to take a full day for the unloading and then reloading of cargo, Julius very kindly granted my request. I had been in Sidon at least twice with Barnabas, and on a few other occasions after that, so I knew a number of the believers there. It was a real encouragement to meet them all again, and although I was required to be chained to my ever-present soldier on all shore leave, I found it most refreshing to talk to those earnest Christians and to pray with them, and to hear their impassioned prayers for me.

Late that night, though, we had to be on our way again, and the twinkling torches lighting the city became mere specks in the darkness as we headed off northeastwards across the vast expanse of the Great Sea.

That first trip lasted far longer than the captain had planned for the winds were against us for a good part of the voyage, but after hugging the coasts of Asia we eventually arrived in Myra, the port of Lycia.

As we were sailing into that busy harbour, I could see Julius' eyes light up, for there, towering above the fascinating collection of craft moored all around, was a huge vessel, one of the biggest I had ever seen. It was a wheat-ship from the Egyptian port of Alexandria, en route to Rome with its cargo of grain to help feed the million or more people thronging the Imperial Capital. It was longer, broader and sat higher out of the water, than all the other boats in the harbour. A Roman pennant fluttered from the top of the tall main mast and there was an elaborate carving of a golden goose surmounting the stern.

From these signs Julius was able to deduce immediately that this particular vessel was one of the many grain ships that were under the Imperial Command, and thus he could use his influence as a senior officer in the emperor's regiment to have his entire party shipped aboard without delay. After a short period of consultation with the emperor's representative and the sea captain on board the ship, Julius ordered that we were to be transferred to this much larger boat, as soon as possible, for she was soon to sail for Puteoli, the port of Rome.

And she did, the very next day.

I thought that there had been a lot of people on board the coastal trader from Caesarea to Myra, but that was nothing to the crowd on board that grain ship. And what a motley crowd we were! Soldiers, sailors, supervised prisoners and subscribing passengers all jostled for space. Luke, who was forever counting and recording things, informed me that he reckoned there were two hundred and seventy six people on that boat, all told. I didn't mind that, for none of them had any other option but to stay there for the duration of their journey, and so I could use my relative freedom aboard to contact as many as I could with the Gospel.

It was fast approaching the stormy season on the Great Sea, and we laboured heavily for those first few days, and when we reached the shelter of the Fair Havens, on the coast of Crete, the captain dropped anchor to consult on his next move. It was by then well on in the year and he had come to the conclusion that we had now no chance of making it to Italy before the fierce winter gales started. We would be forced to stop and spend the winter in a sheltered harbour somewhere.

But which one? That was the question.

Julius, who was the senior man in charge, held a consultation with the ship's captain, the government representative, and myself. As a travelling prisoner I felt honoured to be consulted, but I had often spoken to Julius and he must have remembered how I had told him of a few of my escapades on some of my previous eleven voyages across the northeastern corner of the Great Sea. Perhaps he reckoned that I had more experience in maritime matters than he had!

The captain and the ship's governor had a vested interest in making progress whatever the cost, and they wanted to make a final push for Phenice, a larger port than Fair Havens, and less than three hours sailing time further along the south coast of Crete.

I was against it.

It was very late in the season and having witnessed the sea in all its moods during my many travels I was well aware that in autumn sudden storms could spring up on even the calmest of days, causing absolute havoc.

"I can see that if we attempt to sail on any further, such a voyage could prove disastrous. It will certainly be with hurt and much damage, not only to the ship and its cargo, but also to the lives of all of us on board," I warned them.

But Julius preferred a seasoned mariner's opinion that we could make it, and the ship master's desire to have something more for the company to do all winter than look out at rolling green waves, than the God-inspired intuition of an itinerant prisoner preacher like myself. He ruled that if favourable weather should come we would attempt to reach Phenice.

And a few days later, when a soft south wind, with the warmth of the sands of Egypt in it, engulfed the ship, the captain, and virtually everybody else except me, considered that the long-awaited weather had arrived, and we loosed from our moorings.

For an hour or so, all went well. As we scudded along the south coast of Crete, and rounded Cape Matala, everyone's spirits were high. And I wondered if I had been mistaken to warn against that short trip to a more suitable anchorage.

Then I saw them.

Huge ominous, black clouds had gathered over the hills on the island of Crete, and were bearing down upon us. The soft wind from the south had whirled around within seconds it seemed, to become a howling gale from the north. It pounced on the helpless ship like a mighty eagle, swirling down out of the sky, talons extended, to claim its prey.

The typhoon hit the unsuspecting ship with such force that it threatened to tear the mighty mainmast from its base. The apparently sleeping sea had awakened in sudden anger, sending huge waves washing one by one across our decks.

Brave seamen climbed the rigging and furled the huge sail. It would be impossible to bear up against that wind. Then the captain ordered the men who had been trying valiantly to control the long rudder-sweeps on each side to tie them in and let her drive.

We were now at the mercy of the sea.

For hours and hours we tossed. Then at last out of the gloom we saw an island and calmer water up ahead. This afforded the captain an opportunity to give orders for all non-sailor hands to help in the pulling in of the ship's boat which had been left trailing off the stern for the short smooth sail to Phenice! It was good therapy for all of us to become involved in this activity although it was hard, wet work hauling the waterlogged small boat aboard.

While we had been dragging in the boat the sailors had been wrapping cables below the ship, under the hull, and tying them tightly across the decks. This was, they told us, to pull the timbers tight to prevent leakage. They then took down all other sails, set a storm sail, and allowed our already beleaguered ship with its bruised and battered complement of storm-tossed sailors and seasick passengers to run before the gale.

Next day the crew threw all the cargo, which had been lashed to the decks, overboard.

Then as we ploughed on through mountainous seas the captain ordered that the ship must be lightened even further. Since all non-essentials on deck had already been jettisoned, any sailing gear that was not immediately vital was next to go.

My two companions joined me as all the passengers and prisoners gave a hand to manhandle the mainyard, which was an immense heavy spar, almost as long as the ship itself, into the seething sea.

Our once-stately ship was now a sorry looking sight. Bare decks were washed constantly with cold grey water, which seemed to have an amazing capacity for finding even the smallest chink in her timbers. The tall, stark, sail-less main mast pointed pathetically at a sinister sky.

Day after dreary day dragged on.

Morning, noon and night all looked the same. There was no difference. Each was as grey and threatening as the other.

Those of our number who hadn't lost all interest in living kept looking to the menacing skies for some sign of a change, some ray of hope, some chink of light. Just a short glimpse of the sun or the brief, bright gleam of a distant star would be so welcome. For at least we could then determine our position and direction. Where we were and where we were going. And that would always be something.

But no such help or heartening came.

We just struggled through more and more dark days.

It was not possible to keep the cooking fires going on board, but that didn't matter, for nobody felt like eating, and anyway most of the provisions had already become sodden with the sloshing seawater.

That storm at sea proved a marvellous leveller.

The line of demarcation between soldiers and prisoners, and sailors and passengers, seemed to have disappeared over the side somewhere, with one of those mighty waves which kept washing over us. Everybody was just concentrating on staying alive. We were all drenched through with spray, shivering with cold, unable to rest or sleep, and faint from feeling perpetually seasick yet persistently hungry.

I prayed a lot.

Reading was impossible for two reasons. I felt queasy for most of the time so prolonged concentration was a problem, and I didn't want to expose my precious scrolls of the scriptures to the risk of a soaking with seawater.

Luke and Aristarchus occasionally joined me in prayer when they felt up to it, and these moments of sharing with each other, and committing our lives into the hands of our Heavenly Father, helped us all.

Our continued faith in God stood out in direct contrast to the attitude of all the petrified people around us.

During the early days of the storm I saw many men kneeling down anywhere they could find something to hold on to, in order to prevent themselves being washed overboard, and pleading for preservation to their various gods of wind, and sea, and ships.

There had been no respite, however. And they gave up. Their gods hadn't answered.

Towards the end of our second traumatic week I could see that an even deeper sense of gloom had descended on the already gloomy voyagers. Nobody seemed to want to live any more. They all appeared convinced that we were every one going to die.

I knew differently, though.

And one bleak morning I shared an assurance I had been given, with the drenched and despairing cluster of men on the pitching deck.

It looked as though I was scoring points off them when I began by reminding them that they had ignored my previous advice and sailed from Crete. This was not my intention. My idea was rather to let them know that what my God revealed to me could be relied upon, and thus to establish myself as someone to whom they should pay attention.

Then I went on, "I want you all to take heart, for not a single life is going to be lost on this ship, but the ship herself will be broken to pieces."

Some of the men looked up at me cynically after I had made that bold, and on the face of it, virtually impossible, prediction.

How can he be so sure of that? I could almost hear them ask.

"I know this, " I proceeded to tell them, in answer to their obvious question, "because the angel of God, whose I am, and whom I serve stood beside me and said, 'Don't be afraid Paul. You must stand before Caesar, and as a token of His grace, God has granted you the lives of all those who are sailing with you.'"

The look of hopelessness on the faces before me eased only slightly with that assurance for a monstrous wave crashing against the bow and soaking us yet again with spray, brought a sense of reality to their situation.

Nonetheless, I was not to be deterred.

"Cheer up, men!" I urged them. "I believe God, and if He says it, He will do it! You will see that it will all turn out exactly as I have been told, but we will have to run the ship aground on an island somewhere."

Whether it was my unshaken confidence in God, or just the prospect of a glimmer of hope in a scene of utter gloom, I don't know, but some of those men appeared a bit more positive after that. And they had reason to be, for within days, my prophecy became a reality.

It was about midnight when some of the sailors heard, above the howl of the gale, the far-off boom of breakers on a rocky shore.

"Land ahead!" the sailor on lookout shouted, half in relief, half in terror.

Would we be saved on the sandy shore, or smashed to pieces on the jagged rocks, was probably the question on most men's minds, as they rushed to the guardrails.

"Let down anchors from the stern," the captain ordered, in an effort to slow our progress towards possible disaster.

The anchors held, and we slowed to a stop, at the entrance to a bay. At least we were within sight of land. And that was always something, after two weeks of seeing nothing but angry waves and threatening skies.

Then as a buzz of hope returned to the waterlogged ship I noticed that the weary sailors had devised a plan to ensure their own safety, regardless of what happened to anybody else.. They were lowering our only lifeboat under the pretence of running out anchors from the bow of the ship, but they were actually planning a very selfish escape.

Realizing that those worn out and dead tired men were the only people on board with the complex navigational skills required to beach the ship next day, I went straight to Julius and let him know of their plan.

"If you don't keep these men on board, you can't be saved!" I told him, tersely.

Julius was used to making quick decisions in times of difficulty, and he made one then. He uttered a sharp command, and within two minutes, some of his soldiers used their sharp, short swords to slash the ropes and let the lifeboat fall off to be swept away in the swell.

As hope increased with the break of day, I knew that we all needed sustenance for the day ahead so I encouraged all the men to take something to eat. I found a few flat ships' loaves, which had somehow escaped the searching salt water, and when I had publicly given thanks to God for them I ate a few pieces myself, and then shared them around.

At the beginning I found that I didn't really want to eat, having fasted for so long, but after the first few choking bites I actually began to appreciate the thought of food, and the prospect of strength, again. And it seemed to be the same with the men, in spite of the difficulties yet ahead.

The food had given them renewed strength, and revived hope, and the captain took full advantage of this faint air of optimism, by ordering all hands to work. The sea soaked cargo of grain would be of no use to anybody now, and would certainly never see Rome, so we all carried it up, sack by sack from the hold, and dropped it into the sea.

Our ship would now ride higher in the water and so get as close as possible to land when the captain gave the order to run her up onto the shore.

Having strained his eyes through the rain and murk for some time, the captain decided to sail towards the only sandy beach he could see in the bay before us.

There followed a period of feverish activity as sailors rushed about hither and thither on board, making last minute preparations. Then when everything was in place, all the passengers, prisoners and soldiers stood expectantly, watching.

Suddenly a series of commands rang out from the captain.

"Untie the steering oars! Put up the sail! Cut the anchor ropes, and let her go!" he ordered in short, sharp bursts.

Very soon the sodden ship began to surge forward, gathering speed as the wind filled her sails, but we never reached the planned spot on the shore, for as we were speeding towards it our ship shuddered, then stopped. We had run aground on a mud bank.

So near, and yet not quite there!

Then, unexpectedly, and within sight of safety, another crisis arose. I could see a crowd of the Roman soldiers swarming around Julius, with their hands on the hilts of their swords. It was now their turn to think of their own safety, for afraid of being punished for losing us, I could hear them shouting at their centurion, "We had better kill all these prisoners in case any of them swim to the shore and escape!"

Julius turned and took one long look at me. Killing the prisoners would mean killing me, and he couldn't bear to order that. He and I had become good friends during the trials of the trip, and I had just saved his life, and the lives of his men, less than twelve hours before, when the sailors had tried to jump ship.

"Do not kill the prisoners!" he barked and then turned to take command of the entire situation.

"All those who can swim, jump into the water first, and strike out for the shore!" he commanded.

When this order had been obeyed, all the non-swimmers were instructed as to how to use any buoyant part of the rapidly disintegrating ship as a flotation aid, and they too, made it, eventually, exhausted, to the safety of the shore.

As I looked across at the motley crowd of drenched and shivering soldiers, sailors, passengers and prisoners, sitting or lying, speechless and many of them motionless, in the howling wind and teeming rain, I bowed my head and thanked God for His goodness and His faithfulness.

"I believe God," I had been given the confidence to tell half-crazed men on a half-swamped ship.

And God hadn't let me, or them, down.

All two hundred and seventy six of us had made it safely to land, as He had promised.

But where, on His earth, were we?

Chapter Twenty-Five

ROME AT LAST!

Safe on land we had to make for shelter, so we began to stumble, shivering, up towards the craggy cliffs that bordered the beach. As we struggled along, with the almost exhausted encouraging the absolutely exhausted, I noticed a group of rough-looking men from the island coming down to meet us.

My instant concern was for our own safety for there was not one of us fit to resist any attack, but my fears were ill founded. When I heard them call out, "Come! Come!" in friendly tones, and saw them pointing towards an overhanging rock which would afford us at least some protection from the wind and rain, I knew we were safe enough.

Having dragged ourselves up to the spot to which we had been directed, we were all cheered to find that some of the islanders had already succeeded in lighting a fire, despite the atrocious conditions.

The sight and sound of flames, as they leapt and hissed, and the welcome heat that they afforded us, were very comforting, and we immediately shed our sodden outer garments, and held them up, in turns, before the fire, to dry.

When Julius enquired where we were, one of the local men informed him that we had landed on the island of Malta. Some of our sailors were pleased at this. They knew Malta from previous visits but hadn't recognised it from our angle of approach! It was much more pleasant to sail into its busy harbour, than to be shipwrecked on its rocky shore, they reckoned!

The fire began to die down after an hour or so, and since I was feeling a little less numb by then, I joined some of the others in the search for fuel to keep it going.

I had collected an armful of sticks and brushwood, and as I was about to toss my contribution on to the fire a snake shot out of the pile and fastened its fangs in my arm. It had obviously been dormant for the winter but the heat of the fire had roused it into life.

There were horrified gasps from the watching islanders.

"A murderer!" I could hear one of those close to me remark to a companion. "He has escaped the sea but the vengeance of the gods will not let him live!"

Ignoring their outburst I gave my forearm one good sharp shake and the viper disappeared into the flames.

A sudden silence came over the crowd around the bonfire.

Awestruck onlookers stood staring at me, open-mouthed.

That viper had belonged to one of the most venomous species of snake on the island. Anyone bitten by one of them usually collapsed and died within a matter of minutes.

But I didn't!

I just kept on talking to Aristarchus and a few of my shipwrecked shipmates, as though nothing out of the ordinary had occurred.

In less than half-an-hour they had changed their cry.

"A god! He is a god!" a few of them exclaimed, excitedly. "Snake poison can't kill him! He must be a god!"

I had to smile.

It was Lystra in reverse.

There they had proclaimed me a god before stoning me.

Here they had pronounced me a murderer before deifying me!

I assured the islanders that I was not a god, but a servant of the most High God, and that I would tell them more of the message of hope and salvation, which He had appointed me to proclaim, before leaving their island. I always welcomed any opportunity to tell anybody about my Saviour.

Whether it was my perceived supernatural status, or the concern of Julius to negotiate the safe passage of his prisoners, I was never quite sure, but for the next few days we received preferential treatment.

Publius, who was Primate of the island, and who owned the land on which we had arrived in such an unorthodox fashion, invited us to stay with him, until more permanent accommodation arrangements could be made.

After three days of food, rest and shelter and being attended by the Primate's slaves, I felt really refreshed and ready to serve my Master with renewed vigour.

And the opportunity to do so came with a need that was first brought to my attention by my travelling medical consultant, Luke. He told me that he had just learnt that Publius was very concerned for the health of his father. The old man, according to Luke, appeared to be dying of dysentery.

When I heard of this I asked Publius' permission to see him, and with the consent of Julius I was shown to the room where the sick man lay. When there, I prayed for God's help and healing, and God answered my prayer.

The apparently terminally ill patient was cured.

And that was only the beginning!

When news of that healing spread across the island many others came to be healed. It was a wonderful opportunity to present the gospel of our Lord Jesus to many who had never even heard his Name before, and because of the special ability that God had granted me, to see people healed by His power.

This had a very profitable, and practical outcome too, for grateful former sufferers and their relatives showered us with everything we needed to see us through our enforced winter stay on the island.

This kindness was very much appreciated for we had all lost the few precious possessions we had been permitted to bring with us, in the shipwreck.

And when spring came, and navigation became possible once more, the islanders supplied us with sufficient foodstuffs to last us the length of our next voyage!

Our God had provided for us again!

Throughout our period on the island Julius had been making frequent trips to the harbour, and early in the new year he told us that we would be sailing to Puteoli on the 'Castor and Pollux' an Alexandrian grain ship.

When at last our stay on Malta was over I was pleased to be under way again. And after almost six days spent sailing, or resting in harbours awaiting favourable winds, we approached our destination.

There was an air of expectancy aboard as we turned into the Bay of Naples and saw before us the great bulk of the volcano Vesuvius, its top shrouded in a smoking mist. At the foot of the mountain I was able to pick out the white temples of Pompeii gleaming in the sun.

I was soon to be landing in Italy, after a journey that had taken the most of seven months.

Luke and Aristarchus stood with me at the bow of the 'Castor and Pollux' as she exercised the right, which she possessed as a grain ship of the great Alexandrian fleet, to glide into harbour with her topsails still unfurled.

Many people had assembled on the quay at Puteoli to greet the arrival of the food-bearing ship and her passengers, and they watched eagerly as the sailors guided her skilfully to her moorings.

With all the hustle and bustle as we docked it was more than an hour before we were permitted to disembark, and when we finally did, Julius had some news for us.

We would not, he said, be setting out for Rome immediately.

He had to send messengers ahead to Rome to his superiors, informing them that he had arrived in Italy, and await their further instruction. I was sure, though, that he would probably not mind the delay, for since Puteoli was the first Roman city that he had been in for some time he would be keen to catch up with the latest news of the young and volatile Emperor Nero, and all the gossip of the army.

I was a bit disappointed at the delay at first, but then as with all things, I tried to use the waiting time in Puteoli to the glory of God, and for the support of the believers.

My two loyal companions made some discreet enquiries and discovered that there was a small group of Christians in the city. We made ourselves known to them and they offered us unstinting hospitality during our stay.

When we were there some of the Christians suggested that they should also send an emissary to Rome, not to the Praetorian Guard, but to tell the believers in the capital that I had arrived on Italian shores.

This I was quite happy for them to do, and some of them set off on that mission.

During my week's stay in Puteoli I heard some news which I found rather depressing. The young Nero had become something of a tyrant apparently, killing everybody who stood in the way of his wicked whims, to the extent that he had even ordered the assassination of his own mother, Agrippina, the previous year.

And that was the Emperor to whom I had appealed, and before whom I was to stand trial!

I believed that my trip to Rome was God's will for me, however, and on the eighth day after landing in Italy we began our final part of that most eventful journey.

Just nineteen miles north of Puteoli we joined one of the world's busiest thoroughfares, the Appian Way. This road led south from Rome and was thronged by travellers and traders tramping up and down, galloping horses pulling clattering chariots of the rich and famous, and legions of soldiers marching towards the port of Brundisium, en route to some outpost of the empire.

About halfway along the Appian Way we came to a point where the road ceased altogether for some miles and Julius hired a barge on which we were pulled by mules across the Pontine Marshes.

I didn't like that.

The stifling heat and humidity made me feel ill again, and that, coupled with a growing apprehension as to how I would be received in Rome, not only by the unstable emperor but also by the unknown

Christians there, left me feeling rather dejected. I could see that Luke was concerned about me but I kept assuring myself by assuring him that the will of the Lord would be done.

When we had travelled on up out of the marshes and along the road again as far as the junction town of Appii Forum a pleasant surprise was in store. Our party was pushing on through the town in search of some refreshment when I saw a small group of people become particularly animated as they approached us.

Then I recognised a couple of them. They were two of the Christians from Puteoli who had brought the news of my arrival to their friends in Rome and now this was a reception party out to meet me, still more than forty miles from the city!

How my heart leapt for joy to see them and hear them!

One of my major concerns had been dispelled within minutes as they told me how they had been longing to meet me and also how much they had appreciated my letter of three years before!

It was amazing how that meeting with those believers, most of whom I had never met before, helped raise my flagging spirit! I praised God from the depths of my heart for the warmth of their welcome which was almost like a royal ovation, and for the fact that they had been willing to come so far to demonstrate their Christian love for me.

Ten miles farther on, at a little settlement called The Three Shops, I found a second group of more elderly people awaiting my arrival. It was marvellous to meet them as well!

As we drew nearer the city of Rome I felt a strange sense of fulfilment, of the realization of an ambition, though not perhaps exactly as I had once anticipated it. I would never have chosen to approach the Imperial Capital as a prisoner chained to a soldier, nor though, had I ever envisaged approaching it escorted by a chattering crowd of caring Christians!

The Appian Way was a marvellous road. It stretched for miles paved with square blocks of stone which fitted perfectly, almost as though they had grown together. It was wide enough to allow two chariots to meet and was lined on either side with tombs, some of them huge, built of brick or stone and lavishly adorned.

When I asked one of the local Christians about them he told me that they were a sure sign that we were coming closer to the city. The Romans, he explained, were forbidden to bury their dead inside the city walls, and so the wealthy citizens lined the roads radiating from the capital with their ornate tombs.

The bustle on the road increased as the city came into view and as we passed through the Porta Capena, the gate in the walls that constantly dripped water from the aqueduct running above, and into the swarming streets, I felt a chill of excitement shudder up my spine.

After all the years of trying to picture what it would be like from the descriptions of Aquila and Priscilla and the hundreds of soldiers to whom I had been chained for the previous two years and more, I now had the opportunity to see it for myself.

I had arrived in Rome, capital of the world.

The soldiers, who had been our escorts for so many miles and through so many adventures, parted the crowds to permit the party of prisoners from Palestine pass. I had to be encouraged to keep up with the others as I gazed around at the sheer magnificence of the city. There seemed to be yet another palace or temple or arch or monument around just about every street corner!

How I would love to win that city for Christ!

Our destination within the capital was the camp of the Foreign Legion on the Caelian Hill, and it was there that Julius handed me over, rather reluctantly, I thought, to the commander of the camp, the Praetor.

Whether it was what he had said to the commander before leaving, or whether it was whatever Festus had eventually decided to write in the letter, which Julius had jealously guarded through all eventualities, I could never be sure, but I ended up being very favourably treated by Burrus, the camp commander.

He ordered that I was to be allowed to live, chained to a soldier as always, in a house which I could rent near to the barracks, and that my friends and visitors were to be allowed free access to me at all times.

This privilege of having unlimited access of visitors solved my problem of how to reach the city for my Saviour.

If I couldn't go out and speak to the masses who teemed past my door daily, I would invite them in to speak to me. And even if only one person at a time came I would have an audience of two, for my Roman soldier had no choice but to remain with me!

Since there was a large Jewish presence in the capital I decided not to deviate from my lifelong policy of speaking to the members of my own nation first, where possible. So after allowing myself a short settling-in period I dispatched Luke and Aristarchus across the River Tiber to where many of the Jews lived, with invitations for some of the leaders of the synagogues to come and visit me.

Having been informed by my messengers, no doubt, that I was a former Pharisee and member of the Sanhedrin turned preacher and prisoner of Jesus Christ, many of them came to meet me out of sheer curiosity.

As the representatives of most of the seven synagogues in the city filed in and sat down on the floor around me I noticed the puzzled look on their faces as they saw me chained to a soldier.

When all had gathered I began by letting them know that although I had done nothing to offend the ancient laws or customs of my nation, the Jews had handed me over to the Romans as a prisoner. Having tried me for my alleged offences a number of times the Roman authorities had been prepared to release me, but since the Jewish leaders had opposed this I had felt obliged to appeal to Caesar.

Judging that I had an interested, perhaps even sympathetic, audience in those men, I ended the explanation of my position by drawing attention to their initial point of interest.

"That is why I have invited you here today," I told them, lifting my right hand and rattling the chain that dangled from my wrist. "I am bound with this chain simply because I share the hope of Israel."

And I was pleased at their measured response.

"We have had no letters about you out of Judea, and nobody here has heard any bad reports of you," they said. "We feel that you have a right to tell your side of the story, but as far as this sect of the Nazarenes, to which you claim to belong, is concerned, nobody seems to have a good word of it. If a suitable day can be found, we will come back with some of the others and you can give us a full account of your beliefs."

There was no problem in finding 'a suitable day'.

Any day would be suitable for me, for I wasn't going anywhere!

We agreed a date and early on the morning of the appointed day a large group streamed up to my lodging. As more and more men arrived we had to explain to our Roman guards that this was not a Jewish rescue bid but merely 'a religious meeting'!

When every available corner of my room was crammed with Jewish leaders and teachers I sought to prove to them from Moses and the Prophets, that Jesus Christ was the Son of God and the promised Messiah. I went to great pains to point out that His birth, life, death and resurrection in Palestine did not cancel or contradict the ancient prophecies, but rather fulfilled them. I then proceeded to tell them how Jesus had revealed Himself to me on the road outside Damascus and how that I had spent the remainder of my life happy in His service.

I had barely finished before the questioning began. Some of my listeners had obviously been convinced by my arguments, but others were patently less so. The questioning gave rise to a lively discussion, which in its turn had before evening degenerated into a full-scale debate.

As they trooped out of my quarters late in the day, some of them in angry mood, I summed up their response to my teaching, and testimony of faith in Christ, in words they would all well know from the prophet Isaiah.

"It is true what the prophet said," I called out, exasperated, above the clamour of voices raised in dissent. "Though you hear you will not understand, and though you look you will not see! For the hearts of these people have grown dull. They have stopped their ears and shut their eyes just in case they might see and hear, and be converted and healed!"

"Let me tell you something, men of Israel, " I continued, raising my voice in spite of myself. "The salvation of God has been sent to the Gentiles, and they WILL accept it!"

With that I lifted my unshackled arm and gave it a wide sweep toward the door to indicate the myriads of men, women and children of every nation of the world, passing by in the street outside.

Later that evening, when everyone had gone, and I was left chained to a soldier and deep in thought, I began to reflect on what I had told those Jews, in what would probably be my last encounter with my obstinate nation.

'The Gentiles will accept it', I had affirmed, in my frustration.

And my mind travelled back to all the Gentiles who had done so already.

There were the Syrians and Africans from Antioch, the Lystrians and Ephesians from Asia, the Philippians and Corinthians from Greece, and many whom I had just recently met for the first time in Italy…

The salvation of God would spread even further across the world too, I was firmly convinced.

It would be proclaimed and received as far west as Spain, and north over the Alps and across the fields and forests of Europe. I had no doubt that it would even some day be preached in the remote and savage islands of Britain, right at the outer edge of the Empire.

The Gentiles *would* accept the gospel of Jesus Christ.

For God had assured me they would.

Chapter Twenty-Six

MY PROMISE

Although I suspected that my days of extensive travel, reasoning in synagogues, and teaching in churches were coming to an end, I continued to spread the gospel abroad, and strengthen the Christians where possible, from my lodgings.

I spoke to every soldier when he took his turn at the end of my chain, and a number of them turned to Christ for salvation and actually ended up volunteering for Paul-guard duty! Little groups of them even used to come down occasionally from the barracks in their off-duty hours to ask me probing questions about the Christian faith.

Others, though, were not so happy to be my guards and resented me speaking to them about my Lord. Having presented them with the message of salvation in a simple way that they would understand, I then continued to pray for them, that God would open up their hardened hearts.

The greatest source of comfort and consolation to me in those days of enforced confinement was the constant stream of friends who called to see me. A number of the local believers called regularly, and my travelling companions, Luke and Aristarchus, were very faithful.

As the news of my detention in Rome spread abroad I was occasionally surprised as the days wore on at the effort my friends made to be with me.

I was extremely pleased one day when Timothy turned up. He had, he said, been catching snatches of news of me from different places, and when he heard that I had eventually arrived in Rome he made a big effort to be with me. We seemed to talk without stopping for days after he came, for we had so much to share both of our personal experiences and also about what was happening in all the churches.

Then one day in early autumn, with the stifling heat of the Roman summer over, I heard a voice outside enquiring after me, and since it was a voice I felt I should know, but didn't instantly recognise, I was puzzled.

Who could it be?

My question was answered within minutes, for someone had directed the visitor to my room, and there, standing framed in the doorway, was Epaphroditus from Philippi.

He looked tired but happy, travel-stained but satisfied. His long journey was over. He had found me!

"Epaphroditus!" I exclaimed instantly. "Come in! Sit down! It is marvellous to see you here!"

My friend from far away seemed glad of the offer of somewhere to sit down, and as soon as he had done so he reached into the folds of his robe and produced a bag. Leaning forward he placed the bag at my feet, saying simply, "That is something for you, Paul, from all in the church in Philippi. When we heard that you had been incarcerated in Rome we wanted to send you something to help with your expenses."

I was close to tears.

"It really warms my heart to receive a gift from my dear Philippian friends," I replied, when I had regained control of my emotions. "Do you realize that your church is the only one from which I have ever taken a gift of money? You always give so generously. I could never refuse to accept a gift from your people, although I have in the past refused offers of help from others!"

The coming of Epaphroditus began another prolonged period of filling in and catching up. There was so much I wanted to hear about my friends back in Philippi, where I had seen so many saved on my first visit. How were they all?

It was great to have another companion around to call on me, to talk to me, and to speak to others in the city about my Saviour.

I told Epaphroditus that he could remain with me in Rome over the winter and then return to his home city in the spring. That was my plan, but then something totally unforeseen, and potentially very distressing, occurred.

Epaphroditus took sick.

With all his coming and going through some of the less salubrious suburbs of the city, trying to contact people for Christ, he contracted what Luke considered was possibly Rome fever, a potentially fatal disease.

For weeks he lay in his lodging, seriously ill.

It was a trying time.

Luke, my physician, attended to him as best he could but there were times when even he thought it was hopeless. I was most upset, and in the end, all we could do was pray. And I spent many sleepless hours in prayer, pleading with God to spare the life of Epaphroditus. I was so glad that He answered my prayer, and those of many others in Rome, and our sick friend began to recover.

When he was just about able to be up and about again, though still desperately weak, another messenger arrived from Philippi, enquiring about our patient. They had heard somehow that he was sick, and wanted the latest update on his condition.

Epaphroditus came around to call on me one bright day when he felt well enough and I told him what I intended to do. The Christians at Philippi wouldn't rest content until they had him back with them again, so I would write them a letter, thanking them for their gift and telling them of plans I had to send Timothy to them sometime. Indeed I might even pay them another visit myself, if acquitted of the charges against me.

As soon as Timothy was able to buy a roll of papyrus, we began. I dictated the letter and Epaphroditus and he acted as my scribes.

There were other matters to address also. Some of the believers felt that I would feel cheated and discontent, confined to a room chained to a soldier, instead of being out preaching the gospel and contending for the faith in my former fiery manner. So I assured them that I was perfectly at peace with God and myself and that the things which had happened to me had actually enhanced the spread of the gospel, for a number from the Emperor's household had come to faith in Christ.

Having exhorted them to rejoice in the Lord, agree with each other, think positive thoughts, and display the mind of Christ in all their dealings, I had my friends read the finished letter over to me a few times.

When I was eventually satisfied with it we had a tearful parting in my room, early one morning. Epaphroditus was setting out for home, bearing with him, rolled up and sewn into a protective canvas cover, my letter to the church at Philippi.

God has been so good to me throughout all my life and He showed me a further token of His grace when he sent me another visitor. It was someone about whom I had occasionally, and particularly recently as I had grown older and more reflective, a pang of conscience. I was sitting alone with my soldier one afternoon when Luke came in and said, with a smile, "I have brought somebody to see you!"

He turned around to direct my attention to the door and there, sliding silently, almost apologetically around the corner of it and into my room came John Mark!

For a moment we stood gazing at each other, wondering what to say. I raised my arms, instinctively, as far as my chain would allow me, and Mark just came rushing over and threw his arms around me.

Words were unnecessary.

Tears were the order of the day.

It was such a relief to see Mark again, and how he had changed! We reckoned, when we came to talk about it later, that it was about thirteen years since we had parted in Antioch when I had refused to take him with me on my second preaching tour.

Again there was so much to talk about, and my first questions concerned the condition and whereabouts of the man to whom I owed so much, for his unselfish support in my earlier day, Barnabas. How was he? Where was he now? And what about the trip to Cyprus? How had it gone?

So the days passed.

Then one morning, just as my night guard was changing over with the first shift of the day, a miserable looking, guilt ridden young man seemed to appear out of nowhere, right in the middle of the floor in front of me. I gathered from his appearance that he had probably been sleeping rough, and he seemed almost ashamed to speak to me.

"What can I do for you, sir?" I asked him, to break the awkward silence.

"Are you Paul, the preacher who went around all the cities of Asia telling people about Jesus?" The newcomer answered my question by asking another of his own.

"Yes, I am," I replied, puzzled. "And who are you?"

"My name is Onesimus, and my master often spoke about you. He told me once that he was a Christian for you had told him about something called the way of salvation. When I heard that you were in Rome I thought that I should come and see you. Perhaps you could help me."

"Perhaps I could," I went on, "but I need to know more about you. Who, first of all, is your master?"

"My master was Philemon of Colosse," my vexed visitor informed me, and I noted the past tense. His master *was* Philemon, whom I had led to faith in Christ, years before.

"And why are you not with Philemon now?" I went on with my gentle probing.

There was an awkward silence for a moment and I was suddenly conscious that I must have asked a difficult, or perhaps embarrassing, question.

I noted the tear forming at the side of his eye, and it must have hurt him to make an honest confession to a complete stranger.

"I longed for a better life than that of a slave," Onesimus blurted out, "so I stole from my master and ran away. I sold some of what I had stolen to pay my passage to Rome and now I have nothing. No work, no home, no money, nothing but a guilty conscience."

I felt instantly sorry for Onesimus, for I understood his desire to rid himself of the stigma of being a slave, but I also recognised that he had placed himself in a humanly speaking, almost impossible situation.

Slaves had no rights. A slave was regarded in any household, as nothing more than a tool with a voice. He was an implement to be used, and then discarded after use, like a broken ointment box or a worn out quill.

The anxious young man before me, however, was in an even more precarious position for he was a thieving, runaway slave. Unscrupulous masters had been known to put slaves to death for even less. And the minimum sentence for absconding was to break both legs of the runaway. That, it was assumed, would prevent any further escape attempts.

"Sit down there until I talk to you, Onesimus," I said, kindly. "There are a few things I think you should know. I want to tell you about that 'way of salvation' you were mentioning earlier."

The shamefaced slave found a space on the floor beside me, and we talked.

I recognise that the first need of Onesimus was a change of heart and life that could only come through faith in the Lord Jesus, so I told him about the death of Christ on Calvary to put away his sin. I then went on to explain that if he trusted in Jesus as his Saviour then he could have his sins put away and become a totally new man.

Onesimus must have recalled some aspects of what I was telling him from what he had already heard from Philemon, for I could see him smiling wanly, and nodding briefly at some stages. He just sat on, taking it all in, and interrupting with the occasional question or comment.

And that chastened, contrite slave refused to leave my side until later in the day when he had repented of his sins and believed on the Lord Jesus Christ for salvation!

It was amazing to see an air of settled satisfaction gradually take the place of the tormented expression on the face of the newly saved runaway slave as he began to discover the riches that can only be found through faith in Christ.

The guilty slave, with no earthly right or title to anything, was now a pardoned child of God, and a joint-heir with his former master, of the kingdom of God.

Onesimus remained around with me for days, working willingly with Timothy, Luke and the others, and learning more about the Christian faith from them, as well as from myself.

After a few weeks, however, I pointed out to him that I now felt it was time for him to return to his master, for I believed it to be God's order that wherever possible, restitution should follow repentance.

Perhaps understandably my proposal did not receive either immediate or enthusiastic approval from the new convert. There were, I gathered, at least two reasons for this. He loved being part of the happy Christian community which came and went from my prison room, and he was concerned about his reception in Colosse. What would Philemon say, or do, when he encountered his runaway rogue again?

I told him not to worry about Philemon, for I would write him a letter.

The prospect of a letter of reintroduction, presenting him, not as an offending slave, but as a valued brother in Christ, seemed to appeal to Onesimus. And he agreed to it.

It gave me great pleasure to dictate that letter, too, making a play on the meaning of the name. Onesimus, whose name meant 'useful' had once been useful to Philemon, but had turned out in the end to be useless. He could now, though, as a Christian, become useful once more, not only to Philemon, but to both of us. I also offered to repay any outstanding debts, which he had incurred by his misdemeanours, so that the saved slave could be reinstated to his former position in Philemon's household.

When the letter had been written we had yet another sad parting from my rented house. I was pleased to send Onesimus back to Colosse in the company of Tychicus who was delivering another letter to the church in that city for me, and who would be able to speak to Philemon in person, on behalf of his returning slave...

I would love to have time to tell you about that letter to Colosse, and indeed also the other one that Tychicus took for Ephesus and all the other Asian churches.

But I haven't.

I would love to have time to tell, as well, of my release from that first period of detention in Rome, and of my visit to Spain, and the letters I wrote to Timothy and Titus.

But I haven't.

For things have taken a sudden, and possibly a terminal, turn.

A centurion has just been to my cell, to order that I be prepared to stand trial before Nero yet again. I thought this would happen, and indeed I think I mentioned it in my introduction to these reminiscences.

Luke, who is the only one of all my friends with me at the moment, is sitting here in tears. He is convinced that I will not be reprieved this time.

And if he is right, I am prepared to die.

In fact I said that very thing in the second letter I wrote to Timothy, just a matter of weeks ago.

I told him that I would soon be called upon to lay down my life. The time of my departure was at hand.

Nevertheless, I feel I have nothing of which to be ashamed. I have fought a good fight, I have finished my course, and I have kept the faith, for which I am about to die.

I believe God, and He has assured me that there is a crown of righteousness awaiting me in heaven.

My time is running out, and Luke is rapidly becoming incapable of writing anything more, but there is only one suggestion I would like to make.

If you want to hear what happened in the two years or so that I haven't had time to describe, trust in Christ as your Saviour as I did, serve Him in your life as I did, and I will meet you in heaven when you come.

Then I will tell you the rest.

I promise.